JOSEPH PULITZER

FRONT PAGE PIONEER

April 10, 1847 — October 29, 1911

Like a fiery comet Joseph Pulitzer rocketed across the American newspaper world and changed the course of its history. Reporter, editor, publisher, he became the nation's greatest crusader against corruption; fought for and won our freedom of the press. This is the dramatic story of an idealistic genius who shaped the pattern of present day journalism and who left a legacy to the journalists of tomorrow in the famous Pulitzer Prize Awards.

Books by Iris Noble

Biographies

CLARENCE DARROW
Defense Attorney

THE COURAGE OF DR. LISTER

THE DOCTOR WHO DARED
William Osler

EGYPT'S QUEEN
Cleopatra

EMPRESS OF ALL RUSSIA
Catherine the Great

FIRST WOMAN AMBULANCE SURGEON
Emily Barringer

GREAT LADY OF THE THEATRE
Sarah Bernhardt

JOSEPH PULITZER
Front Page Pioneer

LABOR'S ADVOCATE
Eugene V. Debs

NELLIE BLY
First Woman Reporter

NURSE AROUND THE WORLD
Alice Fitzgerald

PHYSICIAN TO THE CHILDREN
Dr. Bela Schick

WILLIAM SHAKESPEARE

Novels

MEGAN

ONE GOLDEN SUMMER

STRANGER NO MORE

JOSEPH PULITZER

front page pioneer

BY

IRIS NOBLE

JULIAN MESSNER   NEW YORK

Published simultaneously in the United States and Canada by
Julian Messner, a division of Simon & Schuster, Inc.,
1 West 39 Street, New York, N.Y. 10018. All rights reserved.

Seventh Printing, 1967

Printed in the United States of America

Library of Congress Catalog Card No. 57–6837

TO

HOLLY

Boston Harbor was midnight dark. Only the lanterns swinging from the tall masts of ships gave occasional glimmers of light on the waters. Portholes were curtained. This was 1864 and wartime. From the docks the watchman could see only these pinpoint lights of the lanterns, the gray outlines of sailing ships moored at the piers and the ghostly blur of others anchored far out in the port.

Silent as a cat, the boy slid over the side of the big, full-rigged sailing ship halfway out in the harbor. The rope burned his hands going down. The shock of the water made him gasp. It was bitterly cold, but he forced himself to dive down deep, and stay down, swimming underwater like an eel until he was quite a way from the ship. Then his head came up and he sighted for the dock.

Along the worn wharf planks the watchman plodded. His eyes were old. The weather was warm; it pressed down on his eyelids the way his heavy overcoat closed about his old, tired body. If it had not been so, if he had not walked his rounds half asleep, he might have seen the boy swimming not more than fifty yards offshore now and heading straight for the dock. And that would have been a strange enough sight, an alarming sight—in wartime—to have sent the watchman hallooing for the militia to come with guns in their hands!

The boy knew this. He was trying to swim quietly, letting the tide carry him in. He used a breast stroke that kept his arms under

7

the water; once in a while his legs would kick out with a violent splash. He would float then, for a while, fear clutching his cold body like a spasm and stopping his breath, waiting for the shout from the dock or the pistol shot to come zinging out over his head.

He had already come a long way. It wasn't much farther. He could see the gas jets from the lampposts spaced at intervals along the dockway. If he could just hold out—

But for all that the tide was doing most of the work he was desperately, frantically tired. An oilskin bag around his neck held his trousers and shoes. Its weight was like a living thing that pulled him down and slued him around and fought against him and against the lift of the waves. Cold had penetrated deep into his bones. It was beginning to sap the strength of his youthful, undeveloped muscles. He gasped for breath, swallowed salt water and choked; the yellowish wooden pier ahead of him bobbed in his sight and was gone as the waves swept over his head.

He would never reach it! Should he call for help? Take a chance that he would be rescued and not shot at? But that would mean being sent back to his ship. He would *not* go back; it would be better to take a chance of being heard while trying to make it.

Now he was threshing wildly, forcing his tired body through the water. He couldn't wait for the tide. The trembling and flutter of the muscles in the calves of his legs might turn into a cramp. He churned the water, cutting through the waves.

The watchman's head came alert. He heard a splash, then another. He peered out over the rail, but directly over his head a gas lamp flickered and he could make out nothing. The gleam of a white arm and shoulder seemed to him a phosphorescent plume in the shadow of a wave. "A fish," he said, shrugging away the sound of the splashes.

Luckily for the boy, now only ten yards offshore and flailing the water as he came, the silence of the night was riffled with innumerable sounds: the creak of ships tugging at hawser and anchor, the

8

barking of dogs, the sighing of wind through mast and rigging, the stamp of horses in the dockyard stables. The irregular beat of his arms plowing through waves was obscured by these other sounds and the watchman dozed on.

Ten yards. Six—five—three—and just as the boy's right leg cramped in intolerable pain, his left one hit something solid. He clawed at it with both hands, slipped down, found it again, getting splinters in one wrist from the raw water-soaked lumber. A wave raised him and threw him over a crossbar. It was the pier!

He rested a moment, taking deep gulps of air, letting the precious air pump into his lungs. He found he could hump his body over the crossbar. With one hand he massaged the knotted muscles of his right leg until he felt the cramp relax. Then he slowly pulled himself up the wooden post. His head came even with the dock floor. There was a thud of hobnailed boots to the right of him; the watchman's legs came into view. The boy ducked his head, listened to the retreating footsteps as they passed and continued their patrol, raised his head once more to be sure that the other's back was to him, then he was up and over the rail. He ran quickly to a pile of kegs and barrels. There he crouched until the shapeless overcoat and the bobbing lantern had once more turned and passed him. This time his sprint took him clear of the wharf and onto the dirt road to the stables. He tripped and fell, almost senseless, into a huge mound of hay by the barn door.

There he lay. He was unable to move. Deep in this hay he was safe.

When at last he could move and his strength had returned, his first feeling was one of thanksgiving, his second of triumph. He could hardly believe he was alive, but he was! Oh, there'd be a hue and cry for him when it was discovered he was gone, but that would not be until morning and by morning he would be miles away from this city with its odd name of Bost-ton.

To a certain agent on board that immigrant ship, this boy, young

9

Joseph Politzer, represented five hundred dollars in cash, bounty money, to be paid the moment he delivered the seventeen-year-old recruit to a certain sergeant of the Union Army in Boston.

Joseph had discovered the financial deal when the ship was ten days out of Hamburg, Germany. One day he had overheard the agent saying to the captain as they walked past his favorite bulkhead hiding place:

"Five hundred dollars apiece I gets for them. Sergeant Mackay pays it on the barrelhead. This is my fourth trip. One more and I can settle down in Hamburg, a rich man. Every wealthy man's son in New England is looking for a substitute to send to war in his place. There ain't enough substitutes in America, so I dig them up in Europe."

The captain swore in good lusty German. "*Donnerwetter*, it's a dirty business all the same! I don't approve of one man hiring another to do his fighting for him. And if a man's going to risk his life being a substitute in somebody else's war, he should at least get the five hundred for himself."

"Don't you go putting them ideas in their heads, Captain!" The agent was alarmed.

Joseph waited until they left. Then he ran to the steerage. He rounded up the other ten recruits and told them what he had heard. But none of them was as indignant as he. Hiring substitutes was not uncommon in the armies of German princes; they were more anxious to get to the golden land of America than they were cautious of their rights.

"If we all stick together," Joseph raged at them, "we can prove this is illegal! That paper we signed was written in English and none of us could read it. He read it to us. He never said a word about collecting money on us. He said the Union Army needed us so badly they were willing to pay our passage across. I want to join the Army. I want to fight slavery. But no one is going to buy and sell me, either!"

10

His cabinmates were alarmed—at Joseph, not at the agent. "Here! —you'll be getting us *all* into trouble. We signed that paper. We can go to jail if we don't do what he says."

"How? If we all stick together and tell this Sergeant Mackay he has no right to—"

They crowded around him, arguing. "We can't speak a word of English. You think they'll take our word against his? We need him—we don't know where to go or what to do. The soldiers will turn us over to the police or ship us back!"

Joseph saw it was no use. He would have to go alone. But they were probably right about one thing: the Boston soldiers were probably in business with the agent and they would listen to none of the arguments of a boy. He would have to run away much farther—to New York. That was the only other city he had heard of in America.

So here he lay on the warm, dry pile of hay and he just wished he could see that agent's face in the morning! Outwitted! Joseph felt like laughing. He was young and that desperate, fearful swim was soon crowded out of his mind by his triumph. He was a free man, free in America instead of tagging humbly behind a crooked agent like a piece of merchandise for sale. So what if he didn't speak the language and was a foreigner here? What if he was all alone? Hadn't he already traveled all alone from Budapest to Vienna to Hamburg and now across the ocean?

That reminded him of something. Quickly he unrolled the oilskin bag. The shoes and trousers in it were damp and spotted by water that had leaked in, but—yes!—the precious thing inside was safe and dry. He pulled out the tiny miniature in its picture frame and held it to his cheek. It was too dark to see her beautiful face but for the moment he had the real sensation that his mother's cheek was close to his and her smiling mouth brushed his.

It was still dark when he slipped through the streets of the city,

11

keeping to the shadows. By sheer luck he found a southwesterly road out of it. An early-rising farmer stopped to give him a lift.

Joseph hesitated just a second before jumping up to the wagon seat. "New York?" he asked, pointing ahead.

The farmer nodded. "To New York? Sure, it will take you to New York, if that's where you're going. But you have a long way to go, youngster, and you don't look much like you're fixed for the trip. Where's your knapsack? Haven't got a satchel, even? You're wet, boy!—wet all the way through." The big, burly farmer flicked the team of horses lightly with his whip to set them briskly moving, then he turned to study his strange passenger more closely.

"Well, answer me. How come you're wet and walkin' down here this hour of the morning? Are you a bound boy running away? An apprentice running away from your master? Answer me!"

Joseph couldn't understand the words but he recognized the threatening tone. This could be trouble.

"My name is Joseph Politzer. I thank you for giving me this ride and for the courtesy you have shown me, but I have done nothing wrong. I can walk. I am going to New York to join your army. The Union Army. To fight in the Union Army." And with that he started to clamber out of the wagon.

"Hold on!" the farmer yanked him back. "Where you goin'?" Out of the unintelligible language of the boy's words, he had recognized a couple—Army—Union Army. "You're a Dutchman, eh?" Joseph had spoken the German of his native Austria but to the driver of the wagon anyone who spoke that tongue was a Dutchman. "Going to be a soldier, eh, lad? Runaway you be, I'll swear to that, but if it's for the Army I'll keep my mouth shut." He gave Joseph a resounding, encouraging slap on the back. "I've got a son of my own fighting down Pennsylvania way. You go help him, boy, and I'll take you as far as I can on the way."

Reassured by the new warmth and friendliness of the man's tone, Joseph relaxed and looked about him. For the first time since he

12

had landed so unceremoniously on the shores of America he was free to take a good look at the country and savor his strange adventure. The dawn was faintly pink and golden in the sky; mist eddied in fine, steaming wraiths from the hollows but as the pale dawn light touched it, it filtered through and made each dew-laden blade of grass and leaf of maple and elm translucent with shining pearl and green and gold. The wagon rounded a bend and suddenly there was light enough for them to see a white house with green shutters.

"Such a pretty house!" he exclaimed in German.

"Not *haus,* boy. *House. House.* Say house."

Joseph repeated: "House. House." It gave him an idea. He could start right now learning to speak English and his new friend could help him.

For the next ten miles he asked questions incessantly, turning and bouncing in the seat to point: *"Was ist das?"* He wanted to know the name of everything: stone wall, tree, bush, dog, cat, village, store. "Store, store, store," he would chant, then eagerly point to the next thing, a thin, white-steepled church: *"Was ist das?"*

Finally the farmer was exhausted. "Hold on, boy! Give that tongue of yours a rest. Here—" he broke open his own breakfast in the brown paper parcel and shoved cold bacon and hard-boiled eggs and a huge wedge of apple pie at Joseph. "Here. Eat this and stop talking for a minute. Never saw such a one for questions. Makes a man go dizzy, he does, with his *wasisdas!* Never thought I'd turn schoolteacher at my age. No—no!" as he saw Joseph's mouth start to frame a question, full as it was with pie. "Be quiet for a while. *Eat!*"

His gesture was plain. Frustrated, Joseph sank back on his wagon seat, eating in hungry bites and letting his eyes soak up the strange scenery around him.

He was used to farm country. The little town of Makó, Hungary, his birthplace, was the center of grainland, and even though he had lived most of his life in the city of Budapest there had always been family picnics and strolls through the woods and fields near by.

This landscape of America was different. Some of the trees and shrubs were familiar to him but many were strange. He liked the giant elms and the hedges of fiery-tipped sumac, but what he liked best were the neat, stone-walled farms. The peasants here, he decided, lived better than in the poor, thatched cottages at home. At the outskirts of a town a rich carriage whirled past them. Joseph's farmer raised up and yelled angrily after the carriage because its driver, in his thoughtless haste, had showered dust over the wagon. At home in Austria, thought the boy, the farmer would have edged over into the ditch to show his humbleness before any rich man.

The towns he did not like so well. Here was the same picture he had seen all over Europe: a few great houses on the hillside, below them the long, ugly mill on the river with a cluster of shacks around it for the workers to live in.

Before he left home Joseph had not thought much about these things. The Politzers had been a prosperous family in Budapest. Joseph's father, a merchant, had given his family comforts and even a little luxury. Not until his death, until his mother had remarried and a stepfather had come into the home, had Joseph known any unhappiness; not until he had decided to leave, because of the constant quarreling with that stepfather, had Joseph known any such thing as poverty. He had left home with money in his pocket, spent it recklessly, carelessly, and when it was gone he had found that innkeepers who smiled at him with a full purse, kicked him out into the streets when his pockets were empty. There had only been a few coins left when he had met the recruiting agent.

Now all this was behind him. First he would be a soldier, with a soldier's pay, then when the war was over he could make his fortune. Everyone had told him America was the place for that. It was big, raw, new land where luck favored the bold and the daring. He could well believe it was true. Joseph laughed out loud. Hadn't

14

he been smart to get rid of that agent's bargain? And wasn't he here, free and his own master? The very first person he had met in America had been kind to him, had given him a ride and shared his food with him. Huddled in the horse blanket the farmer had placed over his wet shoulders Joseph grinned happily. "This was a *wonderful* country! "House. Dog. Mable dree," he murmured to himself. "Dree—tree. House. Store."

In sheer exuberance he waved a hand at the blacksmith as they passed the open smithy where the fire glowed and the horses stomped outside, waiting to be shod.

While Joseph's eyes were on the scene around them, the farmer studied his passenger with curiosity. He couldn't miss the excitement in the boy's bright blue eyes and the older man smiled to himself in sympathy. He could still remember his own feelings of adventure when he was this one's age. But what a funny-looking scarecrow he was! All wrists and bony elbows and knobby knees and a skinny face that seemed to jut out in forehead and nose and jut back the other way in mouth and chin. His hair was long and black and hung dankly, its ends curling along his high cheekbones. "Hope he knows what he's doing and where he's going. He'd better get to his friends quick, or then city thieves will steal the linings right out of his pockets. They'll know him for a greenhorn the minute he opens his mouth."

He would have been horrified to know that the boy had not one single acquaintance or friend or relative in the whole of the United States.

They reached the village which was the end of the wagon's journey. The farmer led Joseph to a fork in the road and pointed the way.

"New York," he pointed. "Keep right on that and you'll make it. Take care of yourself, son." He gripped the thin shoulder with his big hand and gave the youngster a friendly shake. In his own lan-

15

guage Joseph thanked the kindly benefactor over and over again and apologized for leaving the blanket so wet.

The farmer was touched by the warmth of the gratitude and was moved by a feeling of fatherly pity. A brave, good kid—going off like that on his own! Mixed in with both the pity and the admiration was an uncontrollable desire to laugh. The boy looked so odd, standing there in the road, talking his strange lingo! His suit had dried and shrunk on the long, thin, ungainly frame; even when the suit was new it had been cut to a fashion unknown in these parts and the jacket was too short, the sleeves too tight, the trousers almost skin fitting. They weren't anything that an American boy would wear. And when Joseph, remembering the etiquette his father had taught him, swung his long arms around in a great, sweeping, awkward bow, bobbing his head up and down, it was too much for the farmer. He turned away to squeeze his laughter into a choking wheeze.

Happily, Joseph had no idea of this. He bowed once again in farewell and then hurried down the road. As he went he whistled a gay Hungarian folk song.

It took him nearly a week to reach New York but the journey was surprisingly easy. He had walked many of the miles, been given a few lifts, slept in haylofts and farmhouses, paying for his lodging by chopping wood or carrying pails of water from the pump for the housewife's kitchen. He had improved his knowledge of English and could say such simple phrases as "Thank you." "Work? Any work to do?" "This way, New York?"

The big city, when he arrived there, did not frighten or impress him. It was not nearly as great or as elegant as the old cities of Europe he had known—no big cathedrals here, or castles or fortresses with turreted stone walls to menace the people. There were as many dirt streets as there were cobblestoned ones, more buildings of wood than of stone. He saw a few tall, stately homes—some streets of wealth and many of stores and factories, many more of crowded tenement dwellings. There was no age here, no mellowness, no grandeur. But there was a rush and a crowding and a bustle and hurry about the people in the streets and in the construction of new houses, new buildings all over the place, that he liked. He liked the quick way people talked. He liked the feeling of growth. New York, like himself, was young and alive.

Again the magical words Union Army protected him. A grocery clerk pointed the way down the street; a woodseller stopped to push him in the right direction; a motherly-looking woman fished a paper and pencil out of her deep purse to draw him a rude map. Finally he reached City Hall Park and knew he was in the right place.

All along the green edge of the park were recruiting shacks. Each represented a regiment and each had its own recruiting sergeant or corporal planted outside the door, enticing or bullying the young men as they passed to join their particular outfit.

Joseph hesitated as he passed each one. Which should he join?

Then he saw the banner: Lincoln Cavalry. Almost the only name he knew and could spell in America was that of Abraham Lincoln. It was because of reading about Lincoln that Joseph had wanted so much to come to America and fight in this war. And when the recruiting sergeant spoke to him in German—in the language that was spoken in Austria-Hungary as well as in Germany—it seemed to him a miracle.

"Can you ride a horse, son?" the sergeant yelled at him.

Joseph's heart gave a bounding leap. Could he ride a horse! It was the thing he could do best and that he loved most! That must be what that word cavalry meant—a horse troop. This was surely the place for him.

"Is this—do you want enlistments?" he asked nervously.

"Come in, boy!" a beefy hand propelled Joseph inside the door. "Come in and talk this over. You want to fight for this country, don't you? Just got off the boat, eh?—and eager to show how good

17

an American you can be. Well, you came to the right place. All the men in the Lincoln are good German stock; the company was organized by Germans—Americans now—and you'll find them looking out for you like your own brothers."

There were catcalls and laughs from sergeants in near-by booths.

"Whatya dragging in off the street now, Schmidt? Gets all the foreigners, the Lincoln does—they can have 'em—if that one's eighteen then I'm eighty—if they don't treat you right, sonny, you come over here—"

Sergeant Schmidt firmly closed the door against the good-natured bantering. He placed Joseph across the desk from himself.

"Your name?"

"Joseph Politzer."

The sergeant made such an illegible scrawl that Joseph was to go through his entire military life as Joseph Pouletzes. Protests did no good at all; he was called Pouletzes until after his discharge and at that time he changed it again to spell the way it sounded—from Politzer to Pulitzer.

"Age?"

"Seventeen." He added: "I was born April 10, 1847."

The sergeant made it eighteen for the record. "Your father's name? And occupation?"

"Philip Politzer, merchant. But he's dead." Joseph swallowed quickly. "My stepfather, his name is Max Blau."

"Mother?"

"Her name was Louise Berger before she married my father."

"Any other close relatives?"

"My brother Albert. My older brother and my sister Irma died a few years ago. There's just Albert and me left."

"Nationality?"

"My father was part Magyar, part Jewish. My mother was German. I was raised a Catholic because my mother wished it."

Sergeant Schmidt pursed his lips in a silent whistle. Almost the

18

entire German regiment were Protestant Lutherans; they hated Catholics; they looked down on Austrian Magyars and they despised Jews.

"Where were you born?"

"In a little town called Makó. But when I was six years old we moved from there to Budapest, Hungary."

The officer nodded reminiscently. "I've been in Austria-Hungary. I know Budapest well. Beautiful city. The trees on the avenues, the Danube River running between Buda and Pest—"

A terrible thing happened to Joseph—not so terrible except that it wounded his youthful pride. At the mention of the name a homesickness for Budapest and for his family welled up in his throat so that he couldn't speak. Tears threatened him. All his newly acquired manhood crumpled. He fought not to show it, but the mention of Budapest brought on such a wave of longing and loneliness that he wanted to put his head down on the scarred, battered old desk and cry. A thousand pictures rushed into his mind: the wide, beautiful brown Danube, the narrow, tree-lined, cobblestoned streets, the century-old houses. His small self at eight years walking with his big, wonderful father down Andrassy Street into the market place. The exciting smells of the market— the ripe smell of apples, the woodsy smell of mushrooms still dirty and damp from the forest earth where they had been gathered, the vinegary smell of pickles in tubs. The sight of fat plucked geese hanging to beams. The pretty singsong of the flower girls rising above the noise and the babble and the clamor. And then when he was too tired to walk he was carried home, to be gathered up in the arms of his beautiful mother and comforted with warm *krapfen*, the delicious doughnuts that Lissa, the cook, made so well.

Memories came like little slivers into his mind to prick him: Albert and himself trudging off to school in their short trousers and their round school caps. What a distance those four squares to the gymnasium had seemed then! Now he was thousands of miles

19

away. Albert was still at school there, still coming home to the beautiful mother, still eating *krapfen*—while he was—

"What did you do—run away?" the serogeant asked. He had seen the deep emotion darkening Joseph's face and the effort he was making to keep himself under control.

"No. Not exactly," taking a deep breath. "My father died and my mother married again, a friend of the family's. Max Blau. We got along all right, I guess, but I—it wasn't the same. I couldn't get used to having him there or calling him father. And after my father's death there wasn't as much money as before and it was needed for Albert's schooling. I asked them to let me go; they thought I was going to enlist in the German Army. My mother didn't like it"—there was no need to tell how his mother had pleaded with him not to go—"but I was determined. And when I got to Hamburg everybody was talking about the war in America and it seemed like a good idea to come here."

The sergeant wasn't interested in all these details. The kid's tongue went as fast as a cat lapping up milk, he decided, and he interrupted just as Joseph was getting well launched into an account of all he had seen and felt and heard since he had been in America. "Sign here," he said, curtly, shoving a paper across the desk.

Joseph obediently picked up the pen.

Then he remembered. For a moment a struggle went on inside him. Should he mention the five hundred dollars? Perhaps it would be unpatriotic; maybe they were all volunteers and no substitutes in the Lincoln Cavalry. But, on the other hand, maybe this officer was making money on enlistments, too. If anyone was going to profit by his risking his life it should be himself; the captain had said so.

"What about my five hundred dollars?" He was scared and the words came out in a bluster.

Sergeant Schmidt turned a deep, brick red. "Five hundred—?"

He stuttered: "What—what do you know about that? Who told you about substitutes? I thought you were right off the boat—I thought you didn't—"

Joseph knew he had been right. The sergeant's angry embarrassment gave him away.

"Five hundred dollars. The substitute money, that's right. I don't sign until I get it. Why should you put that in your pocket when I'm the one who will be fighting?"

"Now, that's no way to get along in the Army, starting right off to doubt a man's honesty."

"It's no way to treat me—as if I were a fool!" Joseph flashed back at him. He started for the door.

There hadn't been an enlistment in the cavalry for nearly a week. A certain lieutenant was coming by soon and the sergeant knew he was in for a dressing down unless he could produce at least one new recruit. He called Joseph back. Hiding his greed and his anger he put a comradely arm around the boy's shoulder. "Aw, come on, kid. I was only fooling. Sure you get the money. I was just having my little joke. I'll be sitting here in this nice warm shack while you're out there doing your duty. You don't think I'd cheat a brave soldier boy like you, do you?"

Not until the receipt for the five hundred dollars was in Joseph's pocket would be sign.

"Now you'll take the oath," the sergeant told him.

Joseph repeated, slowly, the solemn words that bound him to serve this America faithfully and well as a soldier. A thrill of joy went through him. They were fine, uplifting words and he repeated them with all his heart and soul. Now he was officially in the troop of the Lincoln Cavalry—

Sergeant Schmidt's legs were planted far apart. His heavy fists were on his hips. The comradely look was gone; a terrible ferocity had taken its place. "And now you're in the Army for good! I'll teach you to get smart with me!" Whack! A heavy hand smacked

21

Joseph on one side of his head. "I'll teach you to talk back to your superiors!" he yelled, landing a blow on the other side of his head. "This may give you some idea of what you have to look forward to!"

And his fist shot out and caught the surprised and unbelieving and helpless Joseph full in the mouth. He fell, sprawling, to his hands and knees.

two

From in front of his own brown, patched tent Captain Ramsay could hear a corporal yelling for Private Pouletzes at the top of his voice. He was too far away to make out the words but there was no mistaking the fury in the tone or the curses that went with the hunt for Pouletzes. That boy was in trouble again!

The captain gave an impulsive movement but Colonel Piel checked him with a hand on his arm.

"Don't interfere, Ramsay."

"But—look, sir, I know you don't like the boy, either, but it's getting to be too much to take. Every day they play tricks on him and every day he has to take this kind of abuse from that corporal or from someone else. And if I'm not mistaken it's worse than abuse. When I saw him last night there was a deep bruise on the side of his cheek. He insisted he fell from his horse but we both knew better. Someone had beaten him. I can't stand by and see a nice kid like that—"

"A nice kid," the colonel commented dryly. "To you he seems an object of pity. You're not attached to this outfit. You're on special orders here. You like to play chess with him. Do you think because he can play chess he makes a good soldier? Ramsay, there are three things I ask of my men: fight well, obey orders, don't talk back to officers. Pouletzes hasn't had a chance to fight yet, but I'm sure if he could outtalk the enemy he'd win the war. All I get are complaints about him: won't obey orders, argues about orders, questions orders and talks back! He's going to be broken, Ramsay, and if that means breaking him the hard way then that's the way it's going to be."

"You forget one other thing. A cavalryman has to be able to ride well and you must admit, Colonel, that boy rides with the best."

"I haven't forgotten," he said bitterly, "how well he rides. The first time I saw him he was riding in maneuvers. I was impressed. I've never seen a better rider. He sat that big bay stallion as if he were part of the horse. I did something I very seldom do. I called him over afterward to compliment him. Pah! On the ground he was the poorest excuse for a soldier I ever saw: couldn't salute properly, didn't know enough to stand at attention, walked—I should say ambled—jerking about as if he were pulled on strings, lost his hat, doesn't look where he's going and splashes mud all over the corporal. When I ask him his name he forgets to say sir and starts some long-winded explanation of how his name is one thing and the Army changed it to something else—Pah!"

Ramsay knew the rest of the story. The colonel, disgusted, had said in a loud tone, loud enough to be heard by the rest of the Troop: "Take that ——— little ——— away from here! I don't want him in my company!"

Those unfortunate words had set their seal on Joseph's fate. What might have been just a joke to be laughed about around the campfires in the evenings had turned into a disgrace for the whole troop. The men couldn't forgive Joseph for it.

The open dislike, the tricks played on the young lad, the brutal hazing by some, shocked and astounded Ramsay. Usually a youngster new in the ranks could expect extra help and encouragement from the older men; outside of himself Joseph had not one single friend.

The dislike was partly due to the colonel's initial contempt for him. And partly it was due to circumstances.

24

The Lincoln Cavalry was already a seasoned fighting unit attached to the Army of the Potomac. The troops had seen bitter action under both Custer and Sheridan. The men were tired. They were also tough and hardened, coarsened by the demands of warfare. They had faced death and seen friends die. They had learned to avoid sensitivity because war demanded a shell around them; some had turned mean and callous and brutal. Just ten days before Joseph had arrived they had fought a terrible battle near Winchester. Casualties had been heavy. Now they were resting—on maneuvers and small, minor patrols and skirmishes—but the letdown of inaction after the holocaust of Winchester had only served to turn their tempers inward. They were surly and intolerant and cranky.

Ramsay also had to admit that it was partly Joseph's fault. The very qualities he appreciated in the young man—his hungry, driving curiosity, his talkativeness, the restlessness of his mind that drove him to maps and books and chess games instead of to the trifling conversation around the nightly campfire—these set him apart and gave the men an excuse to think of Joseph as a conceited puppy who needed some manners knocked into his head. He had the awkwardness and the unsettled nature of a seventeen-year-old who was a boy one minute and a man the next. At best, it was a difficult age. In wartime, with the consistent maturity the Army demanded, it was more than difficult. He was driven to extremes of moodiness and temper and tears and insolence—of defiance that infuriated the men.

He would not hold his tongue. He would not be meek. But there was not enough strength in his arms or sufficient experience in his life to back up his dares. The men called his bluff and, disgusted with him, cuffed him around to teach him his place.

Ramsay thought that it was perhaps a pity that Joseph had had such a kind father and such a gentle mother. They had never prepared the youth for hard knocks. They might at least have

25

given him some inheritance of their own handsome faces! If Joseph had only resembled Franz Roberding, the little bugler of the troop, things might have gone better for him. Franz was rosy cheeked, square bodied, blond and curly headed and he made the men think of their own children at home. He was the favorite, the mascot of the troop; no one was ever rough with him.

That night, for the first time, the captain broke his own cautious rule and questioned Joseph. The two were playing chess by the light of a lantern swinging from the tent ridgepole; they sat on upturned boxes that creaked with every movement they made and threatened to collapse under them. In spite of the discomfort, this tent of the captain's was sanctuary to Joseph.

"What happened today, Joe? I heard that fat corporal yelling for you. Sounded like he was out for your blood."

"Nothing, sir." Joseph kept his eyes on the game. One hand crept up to rub his shoulder.

"Come now—he was making a lot of noise, if it was 'nothing.'"

The boy looked up at his friend. A deep feather of red sprayed itself across both cheekbones, as always when he was very agitated. He tried to shrug his shoulders in an offhand way, but that was a mistake because it made the left one ache again. "I got a reprimand for being in Lieutenant Braun's tent and looking at his maps. Everyone does it; they are no secret material—just maps. But they are out of bounds to me, it seems. The corporal was really sore at me because I questioned an order he gave me this morning. I was right but he thought I was being insubordinate."

His eyes twinkling, Ramsay smiled to take the sting out of the scolding he knew he must give, if Joseph was to stop getting bruises on his face and aching shoulders from blows. "You *were* insubordinate. It doesn't pay to question an order, even if you are right. Not in the Army. It's an enormously bad habit you have, son: always wanting to know *why* an order is given or *what* it is for. Your curiosity may come in handy for you in civilian life, but

26

not here because here you are not an individual. You are a uniform. You step where others do and you move when you are told to and it is not the business of a private in the United States Army to wonder what General Grant is doing in the West and what is happening near Vicksburg and why President Lincoln is doing what he's doing or why Sheridan is taking half of this regiment into Virginia—"

"Is he, sir? Honestly? When is it going to happen? Have we had orders? What will the other half of the regiment—where will they go? Will it be soon? Do I go to Virginia? Is Sheridan coming here first? What will—"

Ramsay threw up his hands in despair. "Stop it! I guess there's no curing you, Joseph. Let's get on with the game."

The news was soon verified. In less than a week the Lincoln Cavalry would be moving out, half to Virginia and the other half to patrol duty in Pennsylvania. The activities in camp tightened up, spruced up, began to rise to a high pitch of excitement and anticipation. The men were glad to think of moving again because it meant the war would be over that much sooner.

Tempers improved. Joseph got fewer cuffs and fewer insults and more good-humored teasing. The slow-talking trooper from Ohio who shared tent space with him even told the boy that he had heard some of the other soldiers say that Pouletzes was a better horseman than anyone else in the whole regiment and the troop should be proud of him.

That was a happy moment for Joseph. Yet the very next day he was in trouble, the most terrifying trouble a soldier could be in.

The reveille bugle had sounded; the troopers scrambled out of their tents for inspection. But this morning Joseph was seconds late and his tunic was still unfastened. The same fat corporal who detested him with a wholehearted contempt that had never changed happened to be doing the inspecting that morning. He called Joseph out of line. The boy stepped forward a pace and saluted.

27

Even the lieutenant who was slowly riding his horse up and down in front of the lines was shocked at the ferocity of the corporal's language.

"Private Pouletzes! Attention!" Striding up to Joseph he flipped open the unfastened tunic. "What the devil kind of a soldier are you? You're a swine! A dirty, lazy, whining, bigmouthed loafer! You're a disgrace to this troop! Did we get you out of bed too soon, huh? Didn't get your beauty rest? Nobody tucked you in last night? And I'm supposed to make a soldier out of a slobbering kid, a draggletail, like you! You're like all the rest of the filthy Austrians—never was a German yet who didn't have to teach you to wash your faces! I'll bet your mother never taught you anything because she never knew anything herself except how to—"

Joseph stepped forward, the white heat of anger rising like a sheet of flame in front of his name. He struck the corporal with all the might of his fist and his anger.

There was a gasp, a quick rustle of movement in the ranks and then absolute stillness. The lieutenant who had been about to stop the tirade froze into immobility on his horse. Striking an officer! No matter how much he had been goaded into it, Joseph's act was the one thing no soldier could do and get away with.

"Private Baines, arrest this man." The lieutenant gave quiet orders. "Corporal"—to forestall the fat noncom who was picking himself up off the ground for a murderous rush at Joseph—"go on about your work. I'll see that Pouletzes is taken into custody."

Joseph was led back to camp, imprisoned in a tent and guarded by an armed sentinel.

He sat on the edge of the cot, his head bowed in his hands, as miserable and terrified as ever a boy could be. Court-martial—disgrace—prison—perhaps it might even be a firing squad. He had heard of such things. This was wartime. He was not a kid playing at being soldier. This was the real thing and he was caught up in a grown-up world with grown-up rules. He wanted to lie down on

28

the cot but he did not dare because then he would give way to his panic or his tears.

But he wasn't sorry. He would do the same thing again if they dared to say a word about his mother, his beautiful, sweet, clean, wonderful mother—

His head went down on the pillow and such loneliness and helplessness swept over him, such a longing to hear her soothing voice and to have her tender hands touch his face in comfort that he was forced to grind his face into the dirty ticking to keep from moaning out loud. Tears dripped through his fingers.

Hours went by. His body, finally worn out by the storm that shook it, succumbed to a half-dozing kind of stupor. He was roused to wakefulness by an unaccustomed roar and bustle of sound outside—the sound of hundreds of horses being saddled and hundreds of soldiers on the move. This was strange! It was twilight. Were they going on maneuvers in the dark? He could make nothing of the unprecedented uproar and his nerves were so shaken, so raw, that he mixed up the strangeness outside with danger to himself. His tortured mind went round in circles again: court-martial—disgrace—prison—or—firing squad?

Why didn't they come? Why did they just let him lie there to sweat it out?

And then, in the next breath, he was wishing desperately that they would never come, that they would just forget him and leave him alone. At that moment he heard firm steps outside the tent and a low voice speaking authoratively to the guard. Then he saw a hand pull open the tent flap.

Joseph got to his feet. He smoothed down his tunic. He straightened his shoulders into a rigid mold and held his eyes up, staring. He waited.

When he saw it was Captain Ramsay and not a military guard detachment, his heart gave a great and wondering leap. The officer's face was grave and stern.

29

"Well, Joseph, you've got yourself into a fine mess, haven't you?"

"Are they—do you know what they—is it going to be a court-martial, sir?"

"It was *going* to be. That corporal you slapped was out for your hide. But a delegation of men from your own troop went to Colonel Piel, and Lieutenant Butcher who heard the whole thing put in a word for you."

"Then I'm not going to be shot?"

"Shot! Good Heavens, son—where did you get that idea? Not that men haven't been shot for insubordination before, but hardly a seventeen-year-old private. Prison for a few months or a year was what they were considering. Ah, Joseph, have you been sitting here in the dark actually thinking that?" He reached out and touched the boy's arm lightly and kindly. Then he became brisk. "Actually you are being released because the company is moving out. It would be awkward to have a court-martial just at this time. You're going on patrol duty—to Virginia. This is where we separate, Joseph. I go with Sheridan. Let me give you my last piece of advice: give up your personal battle for the duration of the war, son."

The captain gave him an exasperated, affectionate slap and went out, turning around to say as his good-by: "Keep up your chess game, Joseph. You have a genius for it."

There was hardly time for Joseph to feel reaction of any kind, even relief, from the news. He was hustled outside by the guard, told to saddle his horse in twenty minutes and be ready to ride or be left behind.

He made a vow to himself to follow Ramsay's advice. And for the rest of his time in the Army he succeeded, helped by several circumstances: the tight curb he held on his own tongue, the grudging admiration the men held for his defiance of the corporal and their own realization that he had been goaded into it; the fact

30

that all of them were too busy with patrol or reconnaissance duty or running into small skirmishes. Then came Colonel Hinton.

The colonel was assigned to the troop. His first need was for an orderly and by chance he picked Joseph. He had no special liking for him but he was a just and fair man who asked only that his orderly carry out his duties quickly and with reasonable intelligence.

His new status removed Joseph completely from the fat corporal's vengeance. For the rest of the months of the war until victory, he ran errands, kept the colonel's papers in neat files, carried messages, copied maps and issued orders in the colonel's name. He slept in privacy in a small tent within hailing distance of the colonel's voice and rode close to his heels during actions. Separated from the rest of the camp life he enjoyed a time of peace that seemed to him a miracle of reprieve.

But the brutality he had experienced left its mark on him. He was never to be the same happy, carefree, self-confident youngster who had once ridden with a farmer and seen in every face a friend.

Suddenly the war was over. On May 23, 1865, the Army paraded up Pennsylvania Avenue in Washington.

For Joseph, who rode with his troop for the last time and for the last time guided the big bay stallion in the ranks, it was a solemn and sad moment. The streets were decorated for victory but over the White House the flag hung at half-mast in mourning for Lincoln, who had embodied for Joseph all that was strong and unifying and democratic in America.

On July 7th, on Hart's Island, New York, the Lincoln Cavalry was mustered, paid off and discharged. The men who had families scattered to all parts of the country but the rest of them, with no other ties, drifted into the city of New York.

In a mood of bravado, to show his family how well off he was, Joseph had sent his mother almost the entire amount of the substitution money. But he had his pay and it seemed enough; it was more than he had ever had at any one time and he could spend it as he pleased. He took a room in a good hotel and slept in a soft bed between clean white sheets as late in the mornings as his tired young body demanded. He ate and ate; he went to the finest restaurants—Delmonico's and Rector's and Sherry's—where the well-dressed diners looked with admiration at his worn uniform. He roamed the streets and people stopped him to shake his hand; everyone, it seemed to him, was on holiday. Victory and peace had brought forth a kind of universal brotherhood.

That was at first. By the end of three weeks New York was crowded with ex-servicemen and then things began to change.

It was time for him to look for a job. His choice was limited because he still spoke English so poorly. The Help Wanted section of a German-language newspaper listed an opening for an errand boy in a large department store. It was a comedown from his big, grand dreams, but he had to start somewhere.

He arrived at the store at seven in the morning. To his astonishment there were twenty men in uniform ahead of him and in less than three minutes there were fifty behind him in line. The manager came out and told them that the job had been filled the night before. He gave them some advice:

"Why don't you men go home to your families? There aren't going to be enough jobs in this city for even a small percentage of you. Every day I get applications. There just isn't any work."

"Where we gonna go, mister?" one asked. And another: "I haven't got any family any place. My wife died while I was in the Army and her folks sold the farm." And still another: "My home's in New Jersey. There ain't any work there, either."

The manager shrugged his shoulders and slammed his office door behind him.

Joseph soon found it was true: there just weren't enough jobs to go around but the homeless soldiers had no other place to go. New York was thronged with men looking for work. He took a cheaper room, spent as little as possible for food and was up at dawn hunting the streets for any work he could find.

Poverty or no poverty, his pride forced him to look his best. He could do nothing about keeping his clothes from getting worn thin, but as often as he could possibly afford it he went to his favorite shoeshine stand in front of French's hotel to get his shoes cleaned and blacked.

One day he took his seat on the stand. Next to him was a prosperous banker. On the other side an elegant dandy in a fine coat with an edge of fur on the collar looked over at him and sniffed in disdain. The bootblack polished their shoes first, pocketed their tips and then came over to Joseph.

The rag worked slowly on one shoe, then stopped. The bootblack stepped away. "Look, mister—I hate to ask you this, but would you mind not coming here any more?"

"Why not?" Joseph was able to understand English fairly well by now, even though he spoke it badly.

Covering up his own embarrassment by an anger he did not really feel, the other thrust his chin forward. "Because you're bad for trade, that's why. These rich nobs that come outa the hotel, they don't like to be sittin' next to someone that looks like a bum."

"A bum! You call me a bum! Look—no rags. I sew up holes—"

The blootblack shrugged his shoulders. "I know. I'm sorry to have to do this. I was in the Army myself. But this is my living, buddy, and I have to think of my own wife and kids. I haven't said anything to you before, have I? I've let you come here and never minded when you couldn't tip me. But that overcoat of yours! Both those guys were lookin' at it. Look at it yourself!"

If he couldn't understand all the words, Joseph could understand the gesture. He looked at his coat. Patched and sewn and cleaned as best he could with fragments of soap that came his way, it looked more like a burlap sack than a coat. He couldn't blame the bootblack for objecting to it.

33

"Get outa New York, kid," the bootblack called after him. "Go someplace else—anyplace—it can't be as bad as this."

The incident and the advice made up Joseph's mind for him. He *would* leave this place. There was nothing for him in New York, and he didn't quite know where to go, but about one thing he was certain—it would have to be a place where everyone spoke English and he would be forced to speak English, too.

That same day he met a fellow veteran of the Lincoln Cavalry. He told him of his plan. "Where do you think I should go?"

The habit of playing jokes on young Pouletzes was too strong to be easily broken. "I know the very place for you. All English speaking. St. Louis, Missouri—out west. You go there, young Pouletzes, and you'll thank me—it's the very place you're looking for."

Joseph thanked him. "But that was never my name, you know. It was Politzer, but I've changed it to Pulitzer because that's the way it sounds to people here in America. I'm telling you so if you ever come to this St. Louis, Missouri, you can look me up. Thank you again."

He didn't know it was a joke; that St. Louis, which had been settled by Germans, was still the magnet that drew present-day German immigrants. Its language was German, its customs and folkways were German and its English-speaking community was a small minority.

At the very moment of his leaving New York a letter came from his mother.

"Come home, my son," it read. "You are so far away and we miss you. Business is good once more and your stepfather promises not to treat you as a child any more. He says you may go to the university, as you wished to. Your brother Albert is already attending his classes there. It is not right for my Joseph to be alone in a strange country. . . ."

For a moment he wavered. This Missouri was so far away! All

he had to do was to answer this letter, say yes and they would send him the passage money back to Austria and home. But if he went back to Budapest he would be treated like a child. He would be dependent on his stepfather for his upkeep as well as his schooling. Besides, there was no adventure in going back to the past, back to safety. It would be like trying to wear a suit of clothes he had outgrown.

He made up his mind. The West was the real America, the frontier. That was where fortune waited for the bold.

When Joseph walked out of New York he was down to his last few coins. He made his way slowly across the states the way thousands of other ex-soldiers were doing by walking when he had to and bumming rides on freight trains when he could. His last penny was gone when he reached the Mississippi River.

It was the evening of October 10th. A freak snowstorm had come up. Through its swirling flakes he plodded down the streets of East St. Louis. There was still that enormous, muddy, turbulent river to cross before he could reach the big city itself. Even through the snow he could see, dimly, the lights of St. Louis across the river. They might just as well have been in China for he did not have one cent to pay the ferry charge.

Hungry, cold, frightened at the prospect of spending the stormy night without a rooof over his head, so close to those far banks and yet so impossibly far, he felt his courage completely gone. He wandered down to the ferry. There was no point in hugging those ferry gates. He was ordered away but he could not make himself go. He stayed there, his mind and heart empty, his body freezing, watching the big stern-wheeler ease itself up to the dock between the two rows of heavy piling.

He was so close he could hear the boatmen yelling to each other. One loud voice was calling someone named Johann. "Johann"— the wind blew the words away and then carried them back like a shout—"where—is—Johann? Just when we need him to work—isn't—

told him to be here—nine o'clock—" Then other voices took up the yell for the missing Johann.

Joseph's head, beginning to nod with the cold drowsiness that was benumbing his body, suddenly jerked up. He just realized something. The boatmen were speaking in German!

He pressed himself up close to the ferry gate and called to them frantically. "Hey! Please! Is there a job for me? Do you need help? I've got to get to St. Louis and I have no money!" he screamed the last words at them.

A big stevedore came up to the fence. He took one look at Joseph's pinched face, blue from the icy wind. "Whatya want, kid?"

"A job, please. Anything. I have no money for the ferry; I'll freeze to death here. Haven't you got a job for me?" A fit of trembling shook the thin shoulders in the thin jacket—the overcoat had long since been sold for food.

"Well, you're in a bad way for sure, you are. Tell you what— if that fireman Johann doesn't show up for work in a minute or two you go up to the engineer and tell him you'll work your passage across, with a dollar thrown in. It's tough, hard work. We'll be making a dozen trips tonight—mind you, no hopping off the boat when we get to the other side until the night's over. Come on—tell the engineer Big Adolph sent you." The stevedore made a path through the gate for Joseph to slip by the incoming passengers and waved an okay to the tollkeeper.

The engineer asked him if he could fire a boiler. Since telling a lie was preferable to freezing in the snow, Joseph would have stoutly claimed he could pilot the boat. Since Johann did not show up, he got the job.

He was given a shovel and taken to the boiler which stood on the open deck. His job was to throw coal into the fiery mouth of that furnace that kept that boiler going, to throw and throw and keep throwing without a stop. The ferry was bucking a wind across the river that swept with galelike fury. A lot of power was needed

36

from that boiler, and Joseph was the human force that made that power. He shoveled with all the strength of arms and back; never stopping, he slid the shovel into the pile, hoisted its load in a big sweeping arc and flung its contents into the boiler, over and over again, on and on, with a perpetual motion that became a nightmare to him. The freezing cold was on his back and the roaring, blazing heat from the open furnace seared him in front.

All night long it went on; trip after trip, until he was reeling with fatigue. When the ferry tied up at the St. Louis dock at two o'clock in the morning, Joseph was in a stupor of exhaustion and pain. He stumbled off the boat. Big Adolph gave him directions to a cheap hotel, the engineer pressed some coins into his hand, someone put a cup of hot coffee into his hand and he sipped a little of it, swaying on his feet by the potbellied stove that thawed him into a state of torpor.

Then he was out in the streets. The snow had stopped. The sleeping city was quiet as he plodded up to the gaslight that advertised the hotel Adolph recommended. Vaguely he saw a clerk's face and mumbled his request for a room, then followed the figure of the clerk up the stairs. He remembered nothing more.

three

At six o'clock in the morning a bedlam of noise woke Joseph and brought him in a rush to his open bedroom window. Painful twinges in his back and legs reminded him of last night's ordeal, but he forgot all about them in the vivid, dramatic picture that unrolled before his eyes.

The storm was over. The sun was shining, glittering on the river to his left and on the smoke-streaked city buildings that stretched out flat and far to his right. His hotel was on the slant of the river-bank and the bedlam of noise was coming from the wide, long banks and from the river itself. Boats of all kinds—side-wheelers, stern-wheelers, tugs, rafts, flat-bottomed pole-driven barges—crowded each other at the levees, coming and going, loading and unloading freight and passengers. Stevedores rolled bales of cotton up the wharf. Their work song floated up to him, powerful and steady.

Joseph's hungry nose caught the heavy aroma of molasses and sugar and brine. The wind brought other odors not so appetizing, the mingling of coal tar and pitch and rotting fish caught in the oily scum of the river.

Dressing hurriedly, he ran down the stairs two steps at a time, paid his bill and rushed out into the muddy, unpaved street, almost throwing himself under the wheels of a huge, white, canvas-covered wagon that was lurching its way up from the ferry.

A Conestoga wagon! This was the wagon—becoming rarer every day as the railroads expanded—made famous by the pioneers who used it to carry themselves and all their possessions on the caravans to the uncharted West. Joseph stood and gawked, getting a stern frown in return from the bearded pioneer who drove the wagon and a shy smile from his poke-bonneted wife.

He followed the wagon up the slope to the city. He bought a bun at a bakery and, munching it, walked the streets in a hurry to see everything. St. Louis had something he had never found in any other city: a meeting ground of languid, elegant southerner, smart, brisk easterner and the tough and hardy men of North and West. The streets were as crowded with the picturesque figures of hunters and trappers in buckskin, with army troops, with settler families, as they were with broadcloth suits and dignified beaver hats and hoop-skirted crinoline-clad ladies. Pushing their way with arrogance through the throng were the real lords of the city— the rivermen, the swaggering, roistering men who worked the paddle boats from New Orleans to the far north sweep of the Mississippi. The railroads were threatening their dominion but they laughed at them. Everyone knew that "Ole Miss" would carry the cargo long after those steam engines busted their boilers chugging over the mountains!

There were fine streets of fine-looking business houses. There were libraries and banks and big hotels, evidences of the solid and prosperous citizenry.

History was being made in St. Louis. The end of the Civil War opened up all the West to be free states and industrial states instead of plantation land. It was the biggest expansion boom the country had ever seen and much of it flowed through this gateway city. Trains and wagons carried immigrants from the East. In St. Louis they got their equipment and were on their way to hunt or trap, to find gold, to plow farms, to found new towns and build new states. Streets were powdered to dust or churned into mud

39

under the heavy traffic of ironshod hoofs; cobblestones rang under them like anvils. Joseph found himself pushed right off the busy sidewalk and sank to his ankles in the muddy gutter.

Sight-seeing was fine, but he needed a job. With his last penny he bought an evening paper. There was only one position he could apply for. It read: "Wanted: hostler for mules. Apply Benton Barracks. Ex-cavalryman preferred."

The Benton Barracks, he was told, were four miles north of town. Eating the last of his bun he jog-trotted the whole four miles. When he got there he was told the job was still open—but where were his army discharge papers? How could he prove he'd been in the cavalry?

Joseph ran the four miles back to St. Louis, whirled into his hotel, grabbed his knapsack from behind the counter where he'd left it for safekeeping and ran all the way back again to the barracks. Toward the end it was more of a stagger than a run. But the job was still open; for some peculiar reason there had been very few applicants.

He found out why very shortly. All his life Joseph was to love horses, but mules, he discovered, were a different breed of animal, particularly the stubborn, temperamental Missouri kind. If he was good to them they turned cunning, if he walloped them they waited till his back was turned and then let fly with their vicious hoofs. Even so, he would have stuck it out if the food served to the hostlers had not been so terrible. All six stablemen quit at the same time and Joseph walked out with them.

At least he had a few days' pay. He moved to a lodging-house and gave the landlady almost every cent of it. By nightfall he had another job, operating the gates of the ferry and collecting the fares. By the time the regular gatekeeper had recovered from the flu and was back on the job, Joseph had learned a little more of river ways. He was taken on as a stevedore. This lasted a week. He had not wasted that week; he had talked to everyone he could about prospects and now a driver of a livery hack, delivering passengers to the boats, took him on as a spare driver. Four weeks of that—then back to stevedoring—a month and a half spell as a construction worker on a warehouse building—a couple of days waiting on tables in a restaurant—and so it went for two months.

His landlady tried to advise him.

"Mr. Pulitzer, why don't you do like my other young men? You go from one job to another, hopping around like a flea. Otto Brugel was on that same job building the warehouse like you were but he stays there and now he is to be foreman. You could have been foreman. Otto told me so. And the Irish lad Mickey Kevin, he's saving his money to buy his own wagon. What's the matter, you don't stay at one job?" The big woman was tatting lace doilies and rocking in her favorite armchair. She liked Joseph. He had just brought her another ten dollars to put away for him in her old cracked-leather snapclasp purse. He was now a month ahead with his rent.

He sat down awkwardly on the hassock across the fire from her. The parlor was so crowded with tiny tables and big chairs and footstools and glass-fronted bookcases—every inch of table space packed with pictures in frames and Bibles and fragile porcelain figurines—that he was afraid of a catastrophe every time his elbows and knees tried to maneuver between them.

"But I don't know what I want, the way Otto does, Mrs. Augustus. He wants to be a builder. Mickey wants to have a wagon and a team of horses." Joseph sighed. "When I tell them I don't want to be tied down yet they think I'm just irresponsible. They say I have no future ahead of me, but that's the whole point. Everything is in the future and I don't *know* enough; I haven't seen enough yet to settle down to anything."

She shook her head. "There are lots of jobs right now but that won't last forever. And how are you getting along with the learning to speak English, Mr. Pulitzer? Why should you care? Ten

41

years I've been here and I know enough to talk to the man who sells me milk from his farm, and for the rest good German is all I need to know."

"It goes too slow! If I could get English books to read that would make me learn but I cannot afford to buy them."

"*Buy* them? To the library why don't you go? There you find them free. There you can read them or you can borrow them overnight."

He stared at her. "You mean I can go to the library? But I do not own any property. I do not have anyone to sign for me. Surely they won't trust me with books!"

"In America they trust you," she told him.

There was a long pause while Joseph considered this startling news. Then he raised his eyes from the fire. He took a deep breath. He told her: "I have made a decision. Tomorrow I will go to this library and see for myself. If it is true, then I quit my job. I have enough money to last me a month.'

"For a whole month you are going to read books?"

He nodded. "And look around."

On his way from the lodginghouse the next morning through the streets that led to the imposing building of the Mercantile Library he walked with a new sense of freedom and alertness. "Looking around" might sound forbiddingly vague to Mrs. Augustus but that was exactly what Joseph wanted to be able to do. With his nose buried in jobs he had felt as if he were shoved off into little pockets of the city's life; buried like that, how could he possibly know what other opportunities there might be for him? From the talk he heard around him he knew that miracles were happening in St. Louis. Fortunes were being skimmed off the river trade, from the warehouses growing chunk by chunk around the docks, from the transportation industry, railroads, stagecoach and wagon. Lawyers were in demand; doctors could not keep up with their practices; schools were opening; architects were designing buildings as fast as they could be blueprinted. Most of all, the merchants flourished. For a young man it was a city of opportunity.

It was true, as Otto had said, that Joseph could have been foreman of the construction job. He had refused for the very same reason that had beset him in the Army, his insatiable desire to know *everything*. It just seemed incredible to him that men spent their lives in one narrow slot, their minds restricted to the same path from morning to night, their eyes confined just to the boundaries of their particular job. He supposed that someday he would have to find just such a slot of his own but he didn't want to be trapped just yet. There was no satisfaction to his spirit in thinking that today he would lay a floor of a building, then the walls, then the roof—and next month the same thing all over again.

He wished he could be like Otto. Otto took pride in such good craftsmanship. "I am *building* something. I am building a *city*," he would boast. "What are you ever going to build with your questions and your wondering and your thinking? Maybe a reputation for being a fool?"

It worried Joseph, too. But he couldn't change.

His steps this morning took him to the corner of Fifth and Market streets. There was a new building there, he saw, and noted that painters were busy putting new gold lettering on the windows on the second floor. So these were to be lawyers' offices! In the doorway a well-dressed middle-aged man beckoned to him.

"Come here."

Joseph walked over to him.

"Want to earn half a dollar?" The man in the doorway had sized up Joseph's clean but secondhand, shabby suit. "Only take a few minutes. I want you to take these papers over to the courthouse, to Judge Elber's chambers, and hand them to his clerk. That's all you have to do. Come back here and I'll pay you."

Joseph ran the errand. He was fascinated by the strange, dignified, austere setting of the judge's chambers and by the quiet

43

busyness of the courtrooms. Here was drama going on all around him. Maybe he would become a lawyer. He hurried back to Fifth and Market and walked up the stairs to the lawyer's office.

"Thanks, kid." The coin was slapped into Joseph's hand.

"Do you need an errand boy? Could I work here for you?'"

"Oh, I don't have enough work to keep you busy. Even if you ran errands for all five of us in the suite here we couldn't do more than keep you in pennies. It would be a big help to us but we couldn't afford you."

Joseph thanked him and walked on to the library. An idea was forming in his head, but he would have to see, first, if Mrs. Augustus was right about his being able to borrow books for nothing.

The Mercantile Library, for a frontier city like St. Louis, was nothing short of amazing. It had a collection of books, a wide range of reading and research material and special documents that could rank with the best in the country. It was not so surprising considering that the city was filled with German *émigrés* who had brought with them to the New World not only a hunger for freedom but their high esteem for culture and learning.

Into these big, dimly lit, paneled rooms with their awesome shelves of books ranging from floor to ceiling came Joseph, and it was as if he had come into his own. The librarian was absent that day and the assistant Udo Brachvogel was almost as young as Joseph and with the same keen interest in learning. They liked each other on sight and Brachvogel took pride in explaining that, yes, the library was indeed free and in showing the boy around, even helping him choose the books he wanted.

At lunchtime Joseph went back to the lawyer's and explained his idea.

If he could work for them two hours a day and if they knew they could count on him showing up for those two hours, to run errands or do copying, would they let him study law? Help him to become a lawyer?

They agreed with enthusiasm. They would be getting a clerk for nothing. In those days it was not necessary to attend a law school to pass qualifications to become a lawyer and most of them had started just as Joseph was doing, studying on their own in a friend's office.

And so for a whole month Joseph was free to do what he wanted: read and study. Every morning he was on the steps of the library waiting for Udo Brachvogel to open the doors. If the lawyers—as frequently happened—wanted him to come to them in the evenings instead of the daytime, then he read right through lunchtime, his book propped open in front of him, munching apples. At first it was hard. He made himself read in English, referring to an English-German dictionary he kept on the table. But soon it became unnecessary, except for an occasional word or two, and then he found himself swallowing books at an enormous rate. Through the lawbooks he was studying he was forcing himself not only to read but to think in English.

This was what he had been wanting for so long. He read everything: history, mathematics, philosophy, geography, science. He read Shakespeare and Bacon and Milton and Voltaire but while he enjoyed literature it was facts he was looking for, and those he found in the thick, dusty, undecorated volumes that usually lay undisturbed on the shelves except for the curious or the researcher. Classroom books. Textbooks. Lecture books.

During this month something happened to Joseph that was incredibly wonderful to a lonely young man. He made a friend.

Brachvogel liked him but they had little in common except their liking for books and that was scarcely enough, in the eyes of an assistant librarian with educated friends of his own, to promote any ties outside the library. But one day he did introduce him to Professor Thomas Davidson. Davidson was not much older than either of

45

them, but although he had only recently come from Scotland to teach in the St. Louis High School, in that short period he had already earned wide respect for his profound and scholarly mind.

Impulsively, the professor asked Joseph to drop by his rooms that evening for a chat.

Joseph arrived early. Davidson had almost forgotten his invitation and had just finished dinner. For a minute he was irritated. He loved the quiet time after the evening meal when he could take a beloved book from the case in his study, light his pipe and forget the trials of teaching. Now he would have to spend those hours being polite to this earnest, shy young man who was probably reading in the library because he was lonely and had no other place to go.

But he was surprised. A few skillful questions from him brought out the fact that Joseph had had a limited but good education in Budapest, that he had come to this country on his own initiative, had already served in the Army and was now studying law. Hmmmm—this didn't sound like the usual history of a boy of eighteen. Still being polite, Davidson asked him what he thought of America, the usual question put to newcomers.

"It's a wonderful country," Joseph answered. He cradled his cup of tea in his long, supple fingers and his bony elbows rested on his bony knees. He looked at Davidson with hopeful but distrustful expectation. Would this one let him talk—and answer questions? "But it is full of contradictions. It was founded on ideas of freedom that existed nowhere else in the world and it helped the French to have their revolution. But it tolerated slavery. How could the idea of slavery exist alongside of the idea of freedom?"

"Slavery was not just an idea," Davidson answered, "although to give it respectability men had to claim it was ordained by God and by nature. But basically it was an economic measure to put money into the pockets of landowners. It could not survive because economically it came in conflict with industrial conflicts. There is something of a parallel here, between land wealth and industrial wealth, that happened in the time of Cromwell."

And Davidson began to talk of the beginnings of the industrial revolution. As he went on, his lecture became enthusiastic, not so much from his own interest as from the luminous eagerness in Joseph's eyes and the intelligent questions he asked. From Cromwell they went to Milton, from Milton to Thomas Paine, from Paine to Jefferson.

It was midnight when Davidson came to with a start.

"Grief, lad! I've been gabbling on like the schoolteacher I am; you must be worn to the bone with my meanderings. It's you that is at fault, though. You are too good an audience."

"May I come again, Professor Davidson?"

"Call me Thomas. I shall certainly call you Joseph. And I should like very much to have such another chat with you."

"Tomorrow?"

Davidson opened his mouth to protest, then to his great amazement he realized he was as anxious as the younger man to see him again. "Please do."

They had become friends immediately. Affection and respect grew up between them that would survive to the end of their lives. For the first time Joseph found someone who not only would talk and listen to him but who could talk with real knowledge of what he was saying and answer questions in a way that made sense.

Davidson's knowledge was that of an encyclopedia. He knew a lot about everything. It pleased him to see his young friend's insistence on digging for the absolute facts, the realities of everything they discussed. Joseph's mind was a challenge that sharpened his reading and studying; he had to work hard to "keep ahead of the laddie." It distressed him a little that Joseph did not enjoy philosophy as much as he did. "You are more interested in *what* people do than *why*," he would argue. "Don't you want to think about the reasons why men and women do what they do and live

47

as they live? Why do ideas change?—the concepts of morality and family life and property, why do they change when a country is no longer feudal but capitalist? What is progress? Is wealth progress? Why are a few men wealthy and a lot of men poor? Why does the world say a man should be lord in the house and a wife be humble? Why—"

Joseph was impatient. "Philosophers are a bunch of dreamers!"

"Those dreamers have helped to change history. I think"—whenever Davidson became slightly personal or emotional his Scotch burr was most evident—"I think, laddie, you might happen to make a guid politician. Nay, that is no insult. A *guid* one—a reformer. You are not likely to change history but you may help to make it—a little."

To this man only, Joseph could tell the terrors of his experiences in the Army. The pain and the humiliation had pierced so deeply into his very being that he found himself shaking as he talked.

"That explains it," Davidson remarked quietly but sympathetically. "I wondered why so young a mon as you should shrink so sometimes from a word and have so much hurt in so bonny a face."

"Bonny! They made fun of me for being so ugly."

Surprised, the other man studied him carefully. "You are not ugly. A bit—a bit *knobbly*, I should say. May I take the liberty of suggesting that a diet of apples is not sufficient? You want to grow into those br-r-road shoulders." Privately, Davidson thought Joseph's eyes remarkable in their brilliance and intelligence and was worried at the boy's habit of rubbing them to ease the strain of reading too much under dim, flickering gaslights. He thought, too, that any girl might envy the texture of his skin. The boy had good points, although there was no denying the fact that his cheap clothes still hung on his skinny frame like something tossed on a scarecrow.

The month was sooon up. Joseph went back to the docks for another long spell of stevedoring that stretched into the spring of

1866. He was able to put more advance rent money into Mrs. Augustus's hands.

The lawyers were upset by the change. They hated to lose their part-time and unpaid clerk. They held a council among themselves and one of them remembered that a society had been formed recently by two prominent newspapermen, Schurz and Preetorius of the *Westliche Post*, for the very purpose of helping deserving German immigrants. Who was more deserving than Joseph Pulitzer?

The society placed him as a bookkeeper in Strauss's Lumber Yard. It was easy work and gave him time to spend his dinner hours at the library, his evenings copying briefs and studying lawbooks, and his week ends divided between library and Thomas Davidson. The money was barely enough to keep him alive, however, so when in the fall he was offered a temporary job as warden of Arsenal Island he was forced to take it or he'd be walking the streets without any soles to his shoes or patches for the knees of his trousers.

Arsenal Island was a cemetery. When Joseph arrived there he was unlucky enough to land right in the middle of disaster. A cholera epidemic was sweeping the city. Dead bodies were hauled in endless wagonloads to be ferried across to the island. Joseph had nothing to do with the actual handling of the corpses; he had only to fill in forms and make detailed reports to the Department of Health, but his days and nights were filled with the most horrible, sickening, morbid sights.

"Get the lad out of there!" Davidson descended in wrath upon the aid society. "That is over much for one of such tender years. He canna stand it!"

But Joseph forced himself to stand it. The officials of City Hall begged him to stay, praised him and promised an excellent job for him if he would. So, even though the days were hideous and the nights worse and the danger of contagion an ever-present threat to him, he stayed on the island until the epidemic was over.

The promised job was indeed a big prize. It required courage and brains, but it would bring him prestige and an excellent salary. The Atlantic and Pacific Railroad needed two men to ride through all the Missouri counties, which were mostly wild and unsettled wildernesses at that time, to record its charter into every county's bylaws and thus permit them a right-of-way and privileges that would stand up in court when they began to build their line.

A young Negro, who already knew something of the country, and Joseph, who knew nothing of it, were chosen. On a crisp autumn day they started out on good riding horses, fully equipped for the long months of their journey with rations and money and power of attorney for the railroad in their saddlebags. Both men rode well and for both, in spite of the hardships, it was something of a holiday. Riding all day in the open air brought health back into Joseph's body and his dreams finally stopped being nightmares of death. Over their campfire at night they would talk. Joseph would read aloud until it was too dark to see.

They talked a great deal about the eagerness for education that was sweeping America. "My people, especially," his companion told Joseph, "want to read and write. Now that the war is over Negroes are holding conventions all over the South and one of the things we want most is free schooling for everyone." And Joseph recalled something that Professor Davidson believed: that with railroads and telegraphs bringing people together out of isolation there had come a corresponding need for people to know more of each other, more of what was happening in the world. Newspapers and magazines were springing up overnight.

They did their job well. At each county seat they checked records and got the required official seal on the railroad rights.

Then tragedy struck. Their way had been hard. In most places there were no roads and they had had to force their way through forest and underbrush, over hills and down steep gullies, through blinding rain and storms. At the river called the Gasconade they were forced to swim the swollen floodwater. His Negro companion was drowned. Joseph tried to save him but both man and horses were swept away. He would have lost his own life if a trick of the floodwater had not washed him up on the farther bank.

His papers, in an oilskin packet, were safe. At the nearest hamlet he got help to recover the body of his companion and to bury him, then he bought another horse and continued the journey alone.

When he reached St. Louis he was showered with praise by both city and railroad officials. The charter rights were granted and recorded. But the flattery showered on him was short lived; time after time he went back to their offices to ask for more work and finally he realized they had even forgotten his name.

Back he went to the round of reading, studying law and clerking. His rent once again was paid for several months ahead. He made a few new friends: Dr. George Engelman, the eminent botanist, was introduced to him at Roslein's Bookstore along with Arthur Koeppler, an Austrian artist who had established a comic weekly called *Puck*. The wife of Judge J. G. Woerner, out of sympathy and curiosity for this young man who was reputed to be such a scholar, invited him to dinner on the occasion of his passing his law examinations.

"So now I am a lawyer," Joseph said, with bitterness, to Davidson, "and a lot of good it does me. I couldn't afford to buy a single ream of foolscap, much less furnish an office and wait for clients." He paced up and down his friend's study. Coming to a halt at the potbellied Franklin stove, he gave a moody kick to the footstool in his way and sent it flying against the wall. Like Mrs. Augustus, Davidson trembled for his furniture every time Joseph's long legs got entangled with it.

"Not a word from the railroad company?"

"Nothing. They don't need me; they don't want me. I had such high hopes there, too. It seemed to me that at last I had found an opening. Now there's nothing and it's back to stevedoring in a week for me. I guess people are right. I've got to stop 'looking around' and settle down to any steady job I can find." He picked up a thick scarf and wound it around his neck slowly, his whole face expressing a brooding discouragement Davidson had never seen before.

"Where are you off to now, laddie?" Davidson indicated the teakettle. "Why not stay the evening?"

"Thank you, no. I'll go to the library. I'm not good company tonight, Thomas."

An hour later he was deep in an armchair at the Mercantile Library, his nose close to the pages of the book he was reading. The flare of the gas jets made the words dance on the page. He had been reading steadily and his eyes were beginning to ache. He pushed back the chair to stretch, then rose and made a slow tour of the room. Through an open door to his right he could hear voices arguing, muffled as if their owners were trying hard to remember they were in a public building.

He peeked in. It was the sun parlor and two men were playing chess. Their argument ended, they had bent their heads again in silence over the board. Joseph watched them idly. Suddenly he sprang forward. One of the men had started to make a move with his bishop.

"Don't do it!" Joseph cried. And while the startled player held his chessman poised over the board, Joseph strode to his side. He peered down at the positions on the board. "If you do that, can't you see it will put you in jeopardy?" He pounced, grabbed the bishop out of the astonished hand that held it, replaced it and made a quick move with a pawn instead.

The two players gaped at him in astonishment.

"Don't you see?" Joseph was so intent on the game that it never occurred to him they might think him rude. "Now you can move

52

here"—he illustrated—"and here—and here—and you've won the game."

Both men stared at the board. Then the winner straightened in his chair, plumped back his shoulders and beamed up at Joseph. "You are right! That is just what I meant to do! Emil—this is the first game I have won from you in weeks and see how brilliantly I have it won!"

His friend eyed him sourly. "It was not you who won it, let me remind you. It is not fair," he protested.

"Emil—Emil! Defeat is nothing—not when you lose to such a brilliant play as that! Admit that you have lost to me."

The one called Emil argued again that it was not he but the young man who had made the move. The game should not count. It was not fair. "You did not win, Carl!"

Joseph turned away to go back to his book.

"Come here, young man. I must know such a chess player." The man named Carl called to him. His tone was indulgent and patronizing; though he looked to be scarcely forty years old, there was something military in his bearing, something commanding in his manner, something so distinguished in his face and the way he held his head that Joseph obeyed him as he would have a superior or a father. The two men had been speaking German to each other. Now he switched to flawless, correct English. "Let me introduce myself to you. I am Carl Schurz, and this is my friend and partner Dr. Emil Preetorius. You may have heard of us?" The question had an innocent vanity in it. The two names were well known in St. Louis and Carl Schurz's was known throughout America.

Joseph was overwhelmed. What a crazy fool he had been—to shove himself, uninvited, into the company of such men as these! Carl Schurz was like an idol to him, as he was to almost every young man in St. Louis—every Republican young man, that is. Carl Schurz was one of the founders of the Republican party.

He had been partly responsible for the nomination and the election of Abraham Lincoln. He was United States Senator from Missouri. He and Preetorius owned the St. Louis *Westliche Post*. He had raised the money to form the very Lincoln Cavalry in which Joseph had served; Schurz himself had been a general in the war. It was his society that helped young German lads find jobs—as it had Joseph.

No wonder the German youth of St. Louis worshiped him. Wasn't Carl Schurz one of them? Hadn't he once been a poor immigrant? And now look at him!

Joseph stammered, acknowledging the introduction. "Indeed, I do know of you. I am glad of the chance to thank you—your aid society has helped me find jobs." His face reddened as he admitted his poverty. "Also, you own the *Westliche Post*. I read your paper— not as much as I used to because now I try to read the English papers." Dr. Preetorius' face, round and plump, had a hurt frown at this, but Schurz smiled approvingly.

"As long as it is to change your accent, fine. But don't let those other papers change your politics. Just what *are* your politics?"

"Carl! The young man plays a good game of chess; let him play chess, not fill up his head with your civil service reforms or your bills for Negroes to vote. Come, Joseph—sit down and play a game with Carl. Let him see how he likes to be beaten by an expert!"

Intent on the new game, Joseph was completely unaware of how skillfully the two men questioned him about himself. Dr. Preetorius was interested in the personal side of Joseph's life; Carl Schurz was satisfied with Joseph's Republicanism. When he told them he had been a trooper in the Lincoln Cavalry the partners looked at each other with deep emotion on their faces. The cavalry had been sponsored by them, and they felt a deep emotional tie with anyone who had fought under its banner. But they said nothing of this to Joseph. All their questioning was done with a sensitive regard for his feelings, yet when the evening was over they would have astounded him with how much they knew of him.

They were impressed. Only twenty—almost twenty-one years of age—already this nice young man was a soldier, a scholar, a lawyer—and such a chess player!

They left him to keep an appointment with their editor Louis Willich at their favorite coffeehouse. They had business to talk over with him. A connection between that business and this young Joseph Pulitzer was beginning to form simultaneously, though unspoken, in both their minds.

It was Dr. Preetorius who brought up the possibility. He approached it in a roundabout way. "So you will not have a reporter by the end of the week, Louis?"

"That's right, Doctor. That's what we have to settle. That reporter of ours got a better offer from Cincinnati and he leaves at the end of the week."

"And have you anyone in mind to take his place?"

Willich shook his head in disgust. "There's only one I would even consider. A fellow named Ahrenberg. A man of a lot of experience, but we would have trouble on our hands. He thinks he knows everything. It wouldn't be long before he'd be trying to teach me how to run the city desk—"

The vanity of their editor was his weak spot. He had run things his own way so long he was afraid of change. The two publishers were ready to take advantage of this. They closed in.

"Ahrenberg—ach—so ambitious a man!"

"We met another young man today—"

"A very bright young man, even though he knows nothing of newspapers—"

"That's right. He doesn't know newspapers like Ahrenberg does. Still, if he's willing to learn, willing to work hard—"

"A scholar he is. A good mind—"

"He beat Emil at chess." Schurz put in, in an offhand way.

"He beat you, too, don't forget."

Willich held up his hands to keep them to the point. "But you say he has never been near a newspaper?"

"Is skill and experience everything, Louis?" Carl leaned forward to speak earnestly. "Couldn't you train him?"

The wily, plump Preetorius shook his head. "Carl— Carl! Leave Louis alone. He is right. Better we should hire Ahrenberg. I understand he was so good in his last job they were thinking of making him the editor but the editor was so jealous of him he was fired. But you wouldn't mind him making the suggestions for improving the *Post*, would you, Louis? The paper could stand a good shaking up—"

Willich was alarmed. His worst fears were being confirmed. "Not so fast, please. I didn't say this young Pulitzer was hopeless. With me to teach and guide him and tell him what to do, I wouldn't be surprised if he turned into quite a competent reporter, if he has the qualities you say he has. I have done better with far worse material, believe me. I say let's give him a chance. You have to be willing to take a chance once in a while, Dr. Preetorius. I say we hire him!"

It was decided. When Willich left to look over final preparations for the next day's publication the two partners laughed and chuckled, congratulating each other on how clever they were and how they had slipped one over on their city editor. They sent a messenger to Mrs. Augustus' lodginghouse, to tell their new protégé to be in Willich's office the first thing in the morning. Then they settled down to their nightly game of chess.

four

It was a dazed Joseph who sat across the scarred and battered desk in Willich's office the next morning. He listened to the editor's explanations as if he were in a dream.

"You want the job, don't you, Pulitzer?" Willich demanded, sharply. To himself, he thought this was a mistake. He had been carried away last night by his fears. This new reporter showed nothing of the bright mind that the partners had bragged of; he was an awkward youth and a stupid one, to boot.

"Oh, yes. Yes! Just tell me again what I am to do."

"Well, ordinarily I'd let you hang around here for a few days and get used to the place. But that reporter!—he got wind I had hired you and now he's just taken off. Hasn't shown up. Sent word he was through. So you will just have to start right out this morning covering a story. Now, listen." As he looked at Joseph's face he despaired. Could he possibly make a reporter out of this thin stripling, with that timid mouth and eyes and those hands that were nervously clutching the squirming knees?

"Now, listen," he repeated. "There's been a robbery out at 22 Fourth Street—Roslein's Bookstore."

"I—I know it," Joseph stuttered.

"Good. Hurry out there, get the story of what happened and don't let the newspapermen from the other papers play tricks on you. You get that story. Hear? You—get—that—story! Find out the details. But don't make a nuisance of yourself. If you see a man named Peters, from the *Dispatch,* stick to him. He'll give you the straight goods. Ask him what happened—I guess that would be better than trying to find it out yourself. You ask Peters. Now hurry!"

Joseph ran all the way to the bookstore. There was no time to even think about this incredible thing, this bolt from a kindly heaven that had struck him. He was a reporter for the *Westliche Post!* Only he didn't have the faintest idea of what a reporter was supposed to do.

Roslein's Bookstore was a favorite haunt of his. The proprietor had been kind enough, at times, to sell him unwanted books at half price.

He came upon the scene breathless and panting. Other reporters were gathered in a small, compact knot by the bookstore window. He recognized them by the pencils they flourished and the pads of yellow paper in their hands. He almost ran pell-mell into them. "Mr. Peters? Are you Mr. Peters? Can I see Mr. Peters?"

As one man they turned to stare at him. They were men of sophistication—in their own eyes—proud as peacocks of their profession and condescending to anyone out of it. Like a badge of their trade, they were dressed very much alike in the loose ulster overcoat or the Inverness cape so fashionable then, their pork pie hats carelessly, jauntily set at the correct rakish angle. Some of them even sported gloves and canes. They cultivated a languishing pose. As was their usual habit, they had sent in one of their number to get the facts from the policeman in charge. They were waiting outside to pool their information.

"Why do you want Peters?" one of them asked. He bit the end off a long, slender cigar and raised an eyebrow at the perspiring Joseph. "He's inside the store."

"I'm the new reporter from the *Westliche Post.* I—"

But just then a man strolled out of Roslein's.

58

"Here it is, fellows," he drawled. "Not much to go on. Job was done early this morning before Roslein got here. Latch on the door was forced. Safe broken into, one hundred and seventy-five dollars gone. Suspect is a tall blond man that old Roslein saw hanging about the shop late last night for no good reason. Constable surmises he is the culprit and a search is about to go out for a tall blond man—oh, yes—scar on right temple. Got it?"

"Got it." The others finished their hasty scribbling and began to saunter off. Joseph looked after them with unbelieving eyes. How could he write a story about that? There must be more to it—maybe he had missed something by coming late. He ran after the one called Peters and pulled his arm. "Please—I'm from the *Westliche Post*. What else is there? What time this morning did it happen? Why do they suspect the blond man?"

"Why—?" Peters interrupted an interesting conversation he was having with a friend. "I don't know what you mean. I gave you the story. That's all there is to it."

Joseph was left staring after them. It was all right for them, perhaps. They were experienced and maybe they could take those simple facts and dress them up into a story. But if he took those few, bare notes back to Willich, he'd be fired. No question of it, he'd be fired. Besides, his own curiosity was aroused. He just had to find out more of what had happened.

And Willich was in a hurry for this!

He dashed back into Roslein's, nearly knocking down the portly figure of the policeman.

"Watch where you're going. This store is closed. Police orders. Get out!" came the sharp command.

"I'm from the *Westliche Post*."

"Just gave all the information to the gentlemen of the press. If you want to know how to spell my name correctly, it's Backus—B-a-c-k-u-s. Now you'll have to get out."

Tiny and stooped, the proprietor of the shop smiled up at

59

Joseph. "Its all right, Constable. I know Mr. Pulitzer. I did not know you had a new position, though. Perhaps you came too late to confer with your colleagues outside? As a favor to me, Constable, I would like you to give this young man special consideration."

Grumbling, the officer told the story Joseph had heard before.

"What time, exactly, do you think the robbery took place?"

"About six, we place it. The watch had passed here just before that and found the door intact."

"Aren't there a good many people on the street by six? Workmen going to their jobs?"

The constable looked uncomfortable. "Yes. I'm surprised myself that no one saw anything."

"What time did you arrive, Mr. Roslein? Did you notice the door open?"

"I came at six-thirty, my usual time. The door was closed but unlocked. It was not until I opened it that I noticed it had been tampered with."

"And where is John Eggers, your assistant?"

"I don't know," he said plaintively. "He hasn't shown up yet. But he did say yesterday he wasn't feeling well and I noticed, poor boy, that he was upset. So I suppose he is home in bed."

The constable had risen slowly and ponderously from his examination of the safe. "What is this about an assistant? You never mentioned to me, Mr. Roslein, that you had an assistant. Didn't it strike you as unusual that he wasn't here?"

"I just never thought about it. Should I have?"

"Yes, you should have!" the constable thundered. "That one fact missing and I've been barking up the wrong tree. There was something fishy about this all the time. A door broken in from outside and nobody on the street seeing it! The lock on that door not really damaged at all—a poor attempt to make it look like it had been hammered at. And how did a blond stranger open this safe with so little trouble? I ask you! I'll bet my next pair of boots that this job was done by your Mr. Eggers and he caught the seven o'clock west-bound train right after the robbery—and I'll bet, too, we have our hands on him by tomorrow morning!"

"Oh, dear!" Roslein fluttered. "Now that I think of it, John did have the combination to the safe and he has been wanting to go out west for some time."

That was the story Joseph brought back with him—but first, just to make sure, he hired a hackney cab to take him to the railroad station. Yes, a man who answered Eggers' description had boarded the seven o'clock train.

He had enough details to fill half a column. Willich was surprised, but if he was pleased he hid it with crisp orders that kept Joseph running all over the city checking the details of a banquet for that evening, the names of illustrious visitors who had checked into the four major hotels that day, and a report of a new piece of sculpture donated to the city by a generous patron of the arts. Willich made some corrections to his copy but on the whole he had little criticism to make. He was amazed. The young man was not doing badly at all. Joseph's nervousness had worn off and he was displaying an eagerness and a vitality for work that was unusual in reporters.

"It's been the most wonderful day in my whole life," Joseph said to Davidson that evening, exulting. "Imagine them choosing me for such work. Work?—it's not work at all!"

"You don't have to tell me how you like it, Joseph. It shines out all over you. I have never seen you so happy. Perhaps this is just what you have been 'looking around' for all this time."

"I think so, too. I go everywhere—I see all kinds of people. I ask questions—imagine getting paid for asking questions!" He picked up his pencil and thick wad of yellow paper with an air of pride and importance that did not escape his friend. "Will you excuse me? I have to go back to work."

"Tonight, too?"

61

"Oh—Willich doesn't know about it. I wanted to find out about a man named Simpson who registered at the Planters Hotel. The porter told me he thought he was going under a false name and that he used to live in St. Louis and his real name is Leslie Cameron. I want to find out about that."

Davidson watched his friend swing down the street, shoulders back, walking with a new kind of confidence. I think the laddie is growing up, he mused to himself, and maybe I have lost my pupil. It would have been nice to have had him turn into a schoolteacher like me, a quiet life—or a lawyer—but he must go his own way.

The next morning Joseph proudly laid on Willich's desk the story that Simpson was really Cameron, as the porter had thought, and that the mystery man was hiding his identity because he was to be married to a Miss Clara Muller, over her father's objections, a story that had come out after Simpson-Cameron had had too many steins of beer to watch his tongue.

Willich flung the copy aside. He cared nothing about that; he waved half a dozen newspapers at the unfortunate new reporter and exploded:

"You imbecile! You've ruined us! All the rest of the papers say that a blond man did the robbery at Roslein's and what does the *Westliche Post* say? Why didn't you do what I told you to? Why didn't you get the story from Peters?— No, I will not listen to you. You can tell your story to Mr. Schurz himself. I don't want him to think I am responsible for this mess. I want him to know I did my best; I told you what to do—" Still furiously scolding, he pushed Joseph ahead of him up the stairs and into the publisher's office. "Mr. Schurz! Just look at this—here!—this story. I cannot be held responsible if you hire young men without any experience just be-because they play good chess. You forced me to take him—" he was spreading the papers out on the desk in front of Schurz as he spoke. "Now, look!"

Their employer studied the papers. "Hmmm. It does seem as if you have blundered badly, Joe. How could such a thing have happened?"

Joseph tried to explain. He was scared. It was his first lesson in how damaging an incorrect story could be to a newspaper. Yesterday he'd been so sure of himself but now his courage was leaking away fast.

"The policeman said Eggers must have done it," he insisted. "I even went to the railway station to check and I thought that since he had run away it was certain he had done it—"

"I'll do the thinking around here," Willich snapped.

"But it *was* Eggers," a quiet voice came from the doorway. They all turned. It was Dr. Preetorius. "I just met Roslein on the street. He told me Eggers was captured late last night and he has confessed. All the money was on him. I think, Louis, that the *Westliche Post* can run a story tomorrow about how our reporter helped to catch a criminal. We were the only newspaper to have the right story today."

For once the city editor had nothing to say. Tongue tied, he swallowed painfully and went out, motioning Joseph to follow him.

Schurz called out: "Stay a minute, Joe. I want to talk to you." The door closed behind Willich. "That was a good job for your first day. If you are as good at catching big crooks as you are little ones, Joe, I will train you to be a political reporter. Now this," he went on, holding up the copy of the Cameron–Simpson story which had accidentally slipped among the other papers, "I think I know something about this. Cameron is a gambler. He was run out of town once for operating crooked gambling houses. And Clara Muller? Her father is Karl Muller, a responsible businessman. What is more important, he is a police commissioner."

Preetorius looked surprised. Schurz explained the marriage plans Joseph had discovered; then the doctor's face lit up with enlightenment. "Oh! So it is blackmail. If the police commissioner doesn't give Cameron a license for a gambling saloon then Cameron threatens to marry his daughter. That fräulein is silly enough to believe Cameron really loves her. You see, Joe? You have to dig to find out what is underneath."

Joseph nodded. Lesson number two: dig for the facts underneath. "I'll go out and see Mr. Muller. I'll get you the story," he promised.

Both men showed identical shocked faces. "A story? That is not a story. We wouldn't print that."

"But why not? Can't we at least print that this man is a crook who was once run out of town and is now hiding under a false name at the Planters?"

Schurz put a fatherly arm around his shoulders. "Joe—you must learn what goes into a newspaper and what does not. That is gossip. We do not give our readers rumors and speculation. Besides, we might hurt Karl Muller and he is a good Republican committeeman. Tell me, what do you think is the purpose of a newspaper?"

"Why—to give people the news, I would say."

"But what kind of news? We do not have much space. We must select. And there is only one purpose, at least for us. We are a Republican paper; our duty is to the Republican party. Through the *Westliche Post* we try to educate people to the program of the Republican party, to reform and to good government."

If this was lesson number three the new reporter did not take to it very well. He couldn't put it into words but it seemed to him that people liked to *hear* the kind of stories Schurz called 'gossip,' so why shouldn't they want to *read* about them? Why was a story about a Republican committeeman's daughter gossip—and a story about a Democrat not gossip? Didn't the readers have a right to know everything?

But it was not his place to say so.

All that day he kept busy. Willich sent him to City Hall, to the police courts, to the railway offices for news of passengers and to the hotels for news of their arrivals.

After dinner that evening he stretched out on the lumpy feather bed in his room at Mrs. Augustus'. He spread all the city newspapers, one after another, down the counterpane. For a little while he looked at them and gloated over his story of the Roslein robbery and the false report in the other papers. Then he forgot his personal triumph. His eyes grew thoughtful as he studied each newspaper, page by page.

What was the purpose of a newspaper? Schurz had asked him. To print news, he had answered. The two publishers had smiled at him, as if his answer was too simple—almost silly.

Now he wondered about this. The *Westliche Post* was a Republican paper—a radical Republican paper. It featured news about Congress debates, about tariff problems, about the scandals of the big monopolies—railroad and lumber and steel—dictating government policy to President Grant.

The other Republican papers had the same stories on Congress debates and tariff but they praised the Grant Administration.

The Democratic papers also carried political stories mainly, even though their stories did nothing but criticize the Republicans from top to bottom.

But where was the rest of the news? The Roslein story was buried in the back pages. There was very little else that Joseph would call news. Joseph leaned back on his pillow, shoving the newspapers onto the floor. Was it just his vanity that made him dissatisfied? He knew now that Schurz and Preetorius and all the rest of the editors considered political news the only kind fit for the front pages. But Joseph was thinking about the conversations he heard every night around the boardinghouse dinner table. Mrs. Augustus' roomers talked politics, to be sure. But they also talked about the accidents they had heard of during the day, the crimes that were rumored around the city, the little things and the big things that were important to people about their jobs and their lives.

Schurz said that was gossip. Perhaps it was. Perhaps he had no business thinking he knew what was news and what people wanted to read. After all, this was his first day as a reporter and who was he to set himself up against experienced editors? He would just have to stop thinking such things.

Still thinking about them, he got up and wadded all the papers into a big ball and shoved them into a wastebasket.

The next day, between assignments from Willich, Joseph found news stories. Even if they didn't get printed, he couldn't resist finding them. His lawyer friends told him of a bitter fight shaping up between two groups in the City Council over a water-right franchise. He found time to go down onto the docks. Just moseying around there, he got an exclusive tip on the plans for a huge new coffee warehouse to be built that month. On the way back to the office he witnessed a free-for-all fight between two rival gangs of hackney drivers. It wasn't much of a fight—with a lot more words exchanged than blows—and Joseph wrote it up as a comedy story.

He was able to find time for these extra stories because he literally ran all day. When he came back to Willich he was panting, but no sooner had he written his stories than he was out again, investigating a rumor that there had been food poisoning at the County Poorhouse.

It was Preetorius who gave the orders to print Joseph's stories. Willich had come to him, confused. "What will we do with all these? I didn't assign him to pick up such stuff!" Preetorius had read them and liked them. They were well written. They had bounce and sparkle.

"Take out that long serialized travel account of the steamboat journey down the Mississippi." Preetorius told the editor. "It takes three columns on page four and it puts me to sleep every time I try to read it. It's boring. Let's give Joe's stories a chance. The kid deserves it for showing so much initiative."

By the end of two weeks Willich was in a daze. This new reporter absolutely bombarded him with stories. Joseph's news items were too good not to print and they had crowded the editor's own beloved travel stories of life along the Mississippi completely off the pages. From early morning until late at night Joseph was out about the city gathering news that no other paper had thought of. At first it was Willich who ran up and down the stairs, perplexed, to consult with the partners over the stories. Then it became easier to let this brash young man take the responsibility on himself. Finally, on any story of importance or of questionable taste the editor's desk was simply by-passed and Joseph went directly to the publishers on the third floor.

Sales of the *Westliche Post* increased. Circulation figures went up.

Reporters from other papers looked on uneasily, but with laughter at first. That young man would burn himself out quickly—or his publishers would get burned themselves for meddling in things that were better left covered up. Schurz and Preetorius would soon put a stop to this Pulitzer's prying and nosing about, stirring up trouble.

Joseph was no longer quite the figure of fun he had been in the Army but he was skinny and badly dressed. He wore thick glasses, and behind them his eyes gleamed with a fanatical absorption, a single-minded intensity that tickled the sense of humor of his fellow reporters.

Get the story. Get the facts. Get the truth—and all of it. This was the fanaticism of his burning, headlong, never-satisfied pursuit of clue after clue, name after name, fact after fact.

A story would break. It might be a fire in a department store. The newspapermen would gather in a close and friendly knot and leisurely compare notes a comfortable distance from the flames.

Then, around the corner, loping his disjointed, rushing gait and hurrying because he had been halfway across town when he had seen the flames, would come the now-familiar figure of the reporter from the *Westliche Post*. A shout would go up:

"Here comes—JOEY!" It was always good for a big laugh.

"Where've you been, Joey? What's the rush, Joey? Buy us a beer and we'll give you the story—hey, wait a minute, Joey—you'll get your nose burned if you go in there!"

But Joseph Pulitzer was going right past them, edging up as close to the burning building as he could get, buttonholing firemen and store employers and eyewitnesses and everyone he could find—and coming out with discoveries that none of the other papers would be carrying in their pages the next morning.

It wasn't long before city editors, wearing long, sober faces, began to compare the pages of the *Westliche Post* with their own. The next step was to post them, side by side, on their bulletin boards for their reporters to note. And it wasn't long before these editors were furiously raking their staffs: Why weren't they bringing back the stories that this Pulitzer did? Why were they being beaten, time and time again, by this kid? Why didn't they go out and dig up stories as he was doing?

Willich strutted around like a complacent turkey cock, but deep down he was disturbed. No matter how much he might boast, he could not hide the fact that he was not coaching Joseph; Joseph was doing everything on his own. The new reporter had been with the *Post* only three weeks but already he had an authority Willich did not dare question and an open door to the publishers' office on the third floor that not even the editor would dare to claim. For four days running, over half the columns in the entire paper had been written by this one man! Willich scanned the sheets for those four days—stories of fire, flood, tragedy, social doings, crime and politics. How was it possible Joey had had time to find all these and write them all? If this went on, the publishers might feel they didn't need an editor at all.

He'd put a stop to this. "Dr. Preetorius"—he had summoned up enough courage to break in on a publishers' conference—"I don't like to complain, you understand, but I do think I should be consulted on the stories we run. Yesterday three columns were set in type before I ever saw them—oh, it was all right!—Joseph had them okayed by you before he took them down. But I knew nothing of them! He writes badly. I would have rewritten them first. He has no turn for fine and elegant writing. It's not so bad a style for a report of a crime, but this story," he said, pointing to the second page, "is about that banquet of the Turnverein. It's too matter of fact. He tells where it happened and what it was for in the first paragraph, and in the second he just lists the names. Now look at the way this man Peters handled the same story in the *Times-Recorder*: '—the elegant flower of St. Louis society was assembled last night!' . . . hmmmm . . . 'the distinguished guests and the brilliant and eminent speakers sat at the horseshoe table laden with beautiful floral displays and the costliest of fine cuisine'—now that is the way we have been accustomed to writing such a story. This Pulitzer speaks too bluntly."

"I know," Preetorius agreed with his editor, "but Joseph says people read such columns to find their own names printed. They don't want to wade through all this language to find out who was there and what was said. I can't argue with him. People do seem to like it better."

"But it isn't good writing. I always think that we newspaper people are part of the literary world and have a tradition and a standard to maintain!"

"He will learn," Schurz soothed him. "We have an idea, though, we should like to have your opinion about. What would you think of sending Joseph to Jefferson City when the state legislature convenes next week?"

"We have always had a special correspondent there!—oh—just a moment"—this would get the young man out of town and out of Willich's hair— "Yes! I think it is an excellent idea. We will have to hire someone else to take his place here, but even though that means more work for me, I shall be glad to make the sacrifice for the good of the *Westliche Post*. Yes, I think Joseph should go— by all means!"

Joseph in Jefferson City was an odd figure. But before there could be much merriment at his expense there was an almost immediate realization that he was someone to be reckoned with. In this field of politics he really shone. He upset all the old standard formulas for political journalism; he refused to accept the hand-outs of some ward politician and take any advice from them, even when they were promoters of the Republican party which the *Westliche Post* supported. Inside of a month he had beaten his way right into the center of the legislative whirlpool.

He did an unprecedented thing.

It was customary for reporters of Republican papers to attend only Republican caucus meetings and reporters of Democratic papers to attend the Democratic caucuses. These were the meetings of real importance. Here it was that bills would be discussed and decisions made to support or reject; the voting on the House floor the next day was hammered out here. For two weeks Joseph went along with the custom. Then one day he heard the Democrats were to meet in secret caucus.

Everyone was seated when he boldly walked in and took his place at the press table.

"You can't come in here!" the chairman protested.

"Why not? Is there something going on here that you don't want the public to know about? Are you afraid? Anyway, I'm in and I intend to stay in." And he did.

Through a chance-met friend he got himself appointed clerk to the chairman of the State Senate Committee on Banks and Bank-

70

ing. It wasn't much of a job and took very little of his time, but it gave him an entree into special committee meetings that no other reporter had.

He traveled between Jefferson City and St. Louis every week. Most of ..is stories would have preceded him by mail or courier. He came to discuss the editorial policy, but not with Willich. Willich mig t think so. He would hear the door slam and the sound of Joseph's feet hurrying up the stairs; he would run out and try to stop him.

"Joey—just a moment—I want to talk to you about—"

But Joseph was paying no attention. He was not being deliberately rude. His business lay with the third floor and the two publishers. While the editor stared after him with mouth wide open in astonishment Joseph would be striding into the publishers' office, shoving back a chair, opening his portfolio of reports and beginning breathlessly to give Schurz and Preetorius the inside story of what he had just seen in Jefferson City.

If Professor Davidson was responsible for opening Joseph's eyes to the history of the world, to literature, to music, to a wide range of ideas, it was Carl Schurz who was his sponsor in political ideas. From him, like a thirsty plant, Joseph soaked up the principles that made Schurz one of the giants of the political scene—his hatred of graft and corruption, whether inside his own party or any other; his insistence that the rights of the workingman and the small businessman and farmer were just as important as those of the rich monopolists; his conviction that the abolition of slavery was not enough, without full economic and political rights for the Negro people.

It was Carl Schurz's great hope that young Joseph Pulitzer would turn out to be a politician—his kind of politician.

"Our chess player, Emil—that was a good gamble we took with him! I shall have him running for Congress one of these days."

Dr. Preetorius sucked thoughtfully on his pipe. "I doubt that,

Carl. He is interested in politics, yes. But he is different—he is not like us. Do you know what he is? A *newspaper* genius. To us a newspaper is a means to an end; primarily to give people the kind of truth that will help them vote for the right candidate and make the right kind of laws. But to Joey a newspaper is a voice for many things—all kinds of stories, all kinds of facts. He says he thinks we should not only educate; we should be the means of letting people know everything that goes on in their city. He thinks we should even amuse them."

"Amuse them! If people want that let them read *Puck* or one of those other comic weeklies!" Schurz was indignant.

But his partner went on: "I see more of the lad than you do. You are often away in Washington. He is thrilled with his work in Jefferson City but it frets him that Willich has gone back to filling the rest of the paper with travel stories. Joey even suggested—I thought Louis would have apoplexy on the spot!—that we stop printing half the front page in advertisements; move them back to the fourth page and run stories that had excitement, like train wrecks, on the front page instead."

"I hope you are wrong, Emil, about his being a genius. Geniuses are troublesome and dangerous. He could be a danger to us."

"There is even a worse danger."

"What is that?"

"That we might lose that genius!"

The two men would have been still more disturbed had they heard Joseph talking to Judge and Mrs. Woerner that evening at dinner. The artist Koeppler was a guest of the Woerners', too. He amused himself by drawing a quick sketch of Joseph, exaggerating the big head and nose, as he listened to his friend ask a shocking question.

"Why does a newspaper have to support any one political party? Why can't it be independent?"

The portly, dignified judge stared at Joseph. His wife smiled indulgently. Koeppler whistled in surprise, and added a mustache onto his picture to see the effect.

"Joseph," the judge was stern, "you are an excellent reporter. Dr. Preetorius tells me you are the best reporter he has ever known. But I have noticed a tendency in you to get a little too big for your britches sometimes. You're a young man with a fine future ahead of you; I don't want to see you risk that future. Loyalty to one's party is as necessary as loyalty to one's friends."

The judge's wife patted Joseph's hand. She had a motherly liking for him. "I don't think Mr. Schurz would like to hear you say things like that, Joey. It is almost as if you were criticizing him."

Joseph felt their kindly rebuke was well meant, but he was stubborn. "I think Carl Schurz is a great statesman and a great American. But doesn't a newspaper have another kind of loyalty?— loyalty to its readers? To tell them all the facts, unbiased and impartial, and let the public make up its own mind?" He rumpled his hair in frustration. "Let the editorial speak the editor's views. But keep the news pages independent of any party or any special interest—"

"Are you implying that Schurz is dishonest?" the judge was shouting in his anger.

"Not at all, sir! The *Westliche Post* never twists or distorts a story. But it elects—as all newspapers do—to print only those stories which the publisher or editor feels is good for the public to hear. It is true there isn't enough space for everything. But if I were ever running a newspaper—"

"If you ever run a newspaper"—the judge's laugh boomed out, cracking apart the tension that had crept into the room—"if you ever do, you'll have more sense by then and you'll run it just the way it always has been!"

The *Westliche Post* had the reputation of being fearless and incorruptible. Joseph soon earned for himself that same reputation. He was offered bribes and threw them into the faces of the bribers— and printed the story with their names. He became known as a champion of the exploited public. Carl Schurz was proud of him. The pages of the *Westliche Post* bristled with exposés of lobbyists in the pay of railroads and gas companies and banks and manufacturers who wanted bills passed in the state legislature to help themselves at the expense of the public.

Joseph was a new kind of newspaperman. His insatiable curiosity gave him an interest in his work; he was not just a paid employee of the paper; he was as responsible as the editor and the publishers for what went into the *Westliche Post*. In St. Louis and in Jefferson City his name became almost as well known as those of Schurz and Preetorius. He was ridiculed, hated, feared and resented by those he attacked. He was loved by a few close, personal friends.

But between those who laughed at him and those who feared him there was an unspoken conspiracy to "get" Joey Pulitzer.

Their chance came late in 1869. He was now twenty-two years old and had been with the *Westliche Post* for over a year. He had just returned from the sessions in Jefferson City. The only political event of the slightest importance at that moment was the election of a representative from the Fifth District of St. Louis. The post had become open when the incumbent resigned. It was a solidly Democratic district, the Fifth; there was no question that the new representative to be elected would have to be a Democrat.

But, as a matter of form, the Republicans met to choose a candidate. There was no chance of their winning; they were just going through the motions.

The big convention room was stuffy with cigar smoke. On the platform the speaker was droning on and on about the glories of the Republican party. Hardly anyone was listening. Delegates whispered to each other, drew pictures on their programs, took cat naps in their seats and woke up only long enough to applaud one speaker and catch the opening remarks of the next. At the newspaper table the reporters were frankly bored. Someone suggested getting a breath of fresh air and they all trooped out.

The speaker on the platform noticed their leaving and noticed, especially, the tall, gangling form of Pulitzer among them. It gave him an idea. He banged the gavel. Everyone jumped awake. "Listen, fellas," he told them, "let's face it. We ain't got a candidate. I've been making a fancy speech but you know as well as me that we don't stand a chance of electing anyone in the Fifth. We might as well have some fun outa it. Whattya say we nominate Joey Pulitzer?"

For a second there was astonished silence. Then it was broken by a wild whoop of laughter. "I so move, Mr. Chairman!" The laughter became uproarious throughout the hall. "Second the motion!"

"All in favor?" the gavel banged down. "Voted unanimous. The candidate of the Republican party for the Fifth District of St. Louis is Joey Pulitzer!"

The reporters heard the uproar and came running back. Joseph was called, unsuspecting, to the platform. "I give you"—the chairman could hardly speak for trying to keep a straight face—"I give you the Pride of the Party, that fearless newspaperman, that crusader for the rights of the people, the next representative from the Fifth—Mr. Joseph Pulitzer of the *Westliche Post!*"

"Hooray! Three cheers for Joey!—altogether boys—For He's a Jolly Good Fellow—" the audience yelled. The chairman held up his hands for silence. "Let us hear a word from our candidate, boys."

The best part of the joke, of course, was going to be Pulitzer's own reaction to it. The delegates struggled to get their laughter under control. They could see Joseph's scarlet face and they wondered how he was going to wiggle out of this one and keep any dignity doing it.

He stood for a minute, perfectly still. The flush in his cheeks slowly ebbed and left him white and shaken. He was under no illusions. This was a coarse and bitter joke on him. It was a moment of the most terrible pain and humiliation. The jolt was the more severe because he had been too busy to care much what people thought of him. He had believed that he was no longer sensitive to insults; Davidson and others had helped him to believe in himself. Now again, as in the Army, they were stripping him of pride and dignity.

If he had been a weak man or even an ordinary man the bitterness of this moment might have been his undoing. But they had underestimated his strength. He squared his thin shoulders.

"I think I know the spirit in which you have chosen me and I will not thank you for it." By now he spoke English purely and grammatically but when he was deeply emotional there was still a trace of the German in the guttural vowels and the thickening of *t* into *d*. It happened now. "But I believe, even if you do not, that there is a chance to win this election if the candidate will campaign honestly and truthfully and go right to the people. I accept the nomination."

This was a shock. They hadn't meant it to be taken in earnest. In complete silence the delegates watched him leave the hall. Who could have expected Joey to take them seriously? A few titters were heard but were quickly hushed. Sober faced and discomfited, the convention hastily adjourned to wait and wonder for developments.

For a week he let them wonder.

He told Davidson of his decision and asked his advice. What should he do first? "Buy yourself some decent clothes, laddie," came the prompt reply. He did so and was astonished at the difference it made. The past year of eating well on a good salary had put meat on his bones. He was beginning to fill out his big frame at last. And his face, while it still had the high, prominent Magyar cheekbones, was losing the boniness of adolescence and taking on a smoother leanness. It was amazing what a good collar did for that face! What next should he do? "Grow a beard, laddie." And in a short while he had a pointed, reddish, curly beard. It added years to his age.

Now he was ready. He began his campaign.

76

He visited homes. He talked to housewives and their neighbors, to storekeepers and their customers, to small and big crowds on street corners. He spoke both in German and in English. He was surprised to find that so many people already knew his name. "You're the Pulitzer who writes for the *Westliche Post?* You write the stories about those crooks in Jefferson City? You're the one knows all about the graft in City Hall?" His reputation brought him a ready audience. They believed him when he said he would fight dishonesty wherever he found it no matter in which party, even though he ran on the Republican ticket. This was a very different kind of candidate from what the voters were used to. Too well they knew the other kind who gave them a picnic or a barbecue once a year and made speeches extolling the virtues of the glor-r-rious old Republican party or the gr-r-rand old Democratic one.

He was elected. It was an upset that sent a shock throughout the whole of political Missouri.

At that time, with Missouri emerging from backwoods settlements, with settlers moving in to farm and settlers moving out to go west, with railroads threading the whole state, with new towns and cities mushrooming, graft, corruption and bribery and outright thievery of public funds flourished with colossal impudence. There were honest men in office but they were handicapped by having little power. Now another honest man had been elected. This one, however, was to be feared. He had the mighty power of the press behind him.

Pulitzer soon saw that he couldn't correct every evil. Wisely, he concentrated on a few.

St. Louis at that time had a peculiar government; rather, it had *two* governments. The mayor and council were elected. The County Court was chosen, in a strange way, by a handful of residents. It had powers of absolute dictatorship over who should be county officials for poorhouse and hospital and insane asylum, who should

77

be charity superintendent and so on. The County Court had a big treasury, accountable to no one but themselves. Since they gave out contracts for the building of county institutions here was a fine opportunity for graft, and Joseph knew enough to realize the Court was holding a tight lid over a stinking, rotten mess.

He set about to expose them. He was going to lift that lid.

Just at that time a new insane asylum was being hurried along. Several hundred thousand dollars had already been spent. The County Court was congratulating itself that it could go as high as a million without much protest from the public, with a good deal of that million sticking to individual fingers in passing. The contract was let to a Captain Edward Augustine for the building.

Joseph Pulitzer rose on the floor of the Missouri House of Representatives to make his maiden speech. His proposal?—a bill to *abolish* the County Court.

By the time he finished speaking the House was bedlam. Hard names, insults, challenges to duels were being thrown back and forth across the room as supporters of the County Court or the City Council took their stand for or against the bill. It was introduced but not yet passed. Whether they were for or against, big-time political machines were startled. An upset apple cart in one place might eventually tip theirs over, too.

Joseph's friends were alarmed for his safety. "People have been known to murder when a million-dollar profit is at stake. You're a young sprat and the whale could swallow you up in one bite," they warned.

He waged the fight in the pages of the *Westliche Post*. He had visited the half-constructed insane asylum and he had forced the court to disgorge some of its bills and a few of its accounting figures. Even on the basis of this partial accounting it was obvious that the asylum's real cost was only a fraction of the money spent. Where had the rest gone? He attacked Captain Augustine by name, as well as the rest of the county officials.

The Christmas season of 1869 Joseph had spent working in this way. He had managed only a few evenings to celebrate with Davidson and with his friends Judge Woerner and Koeppler, the artist. Now it was January and he was back in Jefferson City speaking and writing to bring his bill out of committee and onto the floor for a vote.

On January 27th he dined at the Schmidt Hotel with another newspaperman. They had finished the main course and were now relaxing over coffee and cigars when a man shouldered his way past the waiter to their table. He was a huge man, muscular and bull necked, and he towered over the slighter form of Pulitzer with a menacing fury.

It was Augustine.

"You called me a crook!" Augustine's bellow could be heard all over the startled dining room. "Well—I'm calling you a dirty liar!"

In those times there was no worse insult, unless it be to call a man a horse thief. A duel was the only proper result of such a challenge. To fight with fists marked one as a common brawler and a hoodlum; guns were the weapon of gentlemen. Augustine was displaying a pistol in a shoulder holster. There was only one thing for Joseph to do. He excused himself to his friend. "Wait here," he said to Augustine, climbed the stairs to his room and got his own pistol. When he returned he called to Augustine so that the other was facing him and repeated the other's words so as to make the duel proper and formal: "I call *you* a liar, Augustine"— and fired.

Whether he was taken by surprise, whether he really did not expect Joseph to be brave enough to stand up to him, was not certain, but Augustine, hit in the leg by the bullet, did not return the fire. He held onto a chair for a second while screams and shouts resounded throughout the dining room. Someone else knocked the gun out of Joseph's hand, and when Augustine saw Joseph unarmed, he leaped on him and unmindful of the pain in his leg beat him over the head with the butt of his gun. Both men were bleeding when they were torn apart.

Walter Gruelle, Joseph's newspaper friend, helped him to his room and bandaged his head. The next day Gruelle's story in the St. Louis *Dispatch* showed his own reactions to the affair:

Jefferson City, Jan. 28, 1870—The exciting topic this morning is the shooting affair at Schmidt's Hotel. I think this is overdone. At least, Pulitzer is blamed more than he ought to be. As I told him last night, after he reached his room, I had a great notion to shoot him for aiming at Augustine's breast and hitting him only in the leg. Bad marksmanship is to be deprecated on all occasions, and when a member of the press—and a legislator, to boot—essays to burn gunpowder I want him to go the whole hog—

The "blame" Gruelle spoke of was the howl that went up from the enemies of Pulitzer and the *Westliche Post*. But almost as rapidly as his flesh wound healed, so did the flurry of excitement die down. In the Police Court he was fined five dollars for violating a city ordinance—shooting inside a closed room. A House resolution to investigate the shooting was tabled for want of support. Powerful friends of Augustine and the County Court did succeed in getting the reluctant police to arraign Pulitzer on a charge of assault to kill, but equally powerful supporters of the opposite faction put up the money to defend him. Prosecution was delayed until finally it was postponed indefinitely.

The publicity over the shooting did almost more than Joseph's pleading and Joseph's columns. It brought home to the public the desperate nature of the grafters; they realized that only big money could tempt men to such lengths as Augustine had gone. The contract was nullified. The County Court was exposed and the Pulitzer bill was passed to abolish it.

When his term of office as legislator was over Joseph received an unexpected and a high honor. Governor Brown appointed him one of the three police commissioners of the city of St. Louis.

He was not yet twenty-four. He had become a state power, a city official, and while he still held the title only of reporter for the *Post,* he was in reality as much of an authority there as were Schurz and Preetorius. The paper had grown in circulation and in stature.

Now the nation was in the throes of a presidential election year. Grant was campaigning for another term. The *Westliche Post* opposed him, joined a splinter Republican group and thumped for Horace Greeley. Joseph, as chief political writer for the *Post,* had become such a popular figure in the minds of the people—his spell as a legislator having built him up as a champion of right against wrong—that he was asked to go out into the state as a campaign speaker for Greeley. Davidson heard one of these speeches and was surprised. He watched the slender figure on the platform outlined in black and white against the flaring yellow torchlights and he marveled. "Such a force in him! Is this the same boy who used to look at me over a cup of tea with his wide, eager eyes and ask me questions till they tripped over his tongue? He is a man, now, and with the strength to lead other men!"

He could lead them to believe in his own sincerity but not to vote for Greeley. Grant won the election.

Schurz and Preetorius called a conference in the *Westliche Post* office. The defeat was a stunning blow to them. They were far more concerned with the political battles they must now face, for their ideals and principles, than they were with the future of the newspaper. However, it was a casualty of the defeat; they saw no hope for the *Post* to continue; they must come to a decision about it.

"Circulation is almost entirely gone. We represent a lost cause in the minds of the public and the public has deserted us," Schurz explained. "Advertisements, of course, went first. No one wants to be associated with a Greeley paper—not with a Grant victory."

Preetorius was gloomy. "We had better sell the *Post* before we get into debt and while we still have some assets."

Joseph argued with them. "It is only temporary. A campaign is forgotten almost as soon as it is over and the *Westliche Post* has a long and good record. True, its reputation has suffered. But if we strike out boldly—stop campaigning for anything except local issues —get stories that no one else will print—I tell you we'll pull through! The readers will come back."

The two publishers exchanged glances. They had gambled once before on this "chess player" of theirs. Maybe he had some new moves up his sleeve. Maybe they should take a chance.

To their great surprise, before they could speak, Louis Willich made his declaration.

"Joe is right. But if it is to be done, then he is the one to do it. I think," he said, swallowing painfully, "that he should be the editor of the *Post*. Not me. I will resign or I will work for him, whichever he wants. Because he is the only one who can save the *Post*."

This from a man who knew he was a competent editor, who was vain and ambitious! It was Joseph's first realization that a man could love a newspaper even more than he loved himself.

Carl Schurz slipped his arm around the editor's shoulders. "That is generous of you, Louis," he said, "but not necessary. Emil and I realize, too, that Joseph is the one to run this paper. He can do it best, not as editor, but as publisher and part owner. We three are getting older. He is young and vigorous and filled with new ideas." He smiled. "Let Joey do the worrying for all of us."

Joseph was stunned. The others could not possibly have understood what this meant to him. At that moment his ambitions took on a clarity he had not been sure of before. No political victory, no political job, no success as a lawyer could possibly have stirred the wild joy that was beating inside of him now. But the partners took his stunned silence for deliberation and they hastened to assure him:

"We will let you buy in with us on very liberal terms, Joe! For practically nothing. You have saved something, surely. A few thousand dollars? Whatever you have will be all right with us."

He pulled himself together. "Very well. I accept. But if I take the responsibility I must also have the authority. I must have the final word on policy."

"Didn't I tell you, Carl?" Dr. Preetorius got up to shake hands with their new partner. "Always the chess player, this Joe. Always a move ahead of us. A free hand you will have—but just be careful you don't sweep us all off the board!"

five

The Pulitzer regime lasted only a few short months before Schurz and Preetorius—more frightened than ever—grabbed their beloved *Westliche Post* away from Joseph.

In those months the *Post* regained its lost circulation and even gained new readers; to do this Joseph shook up the paper from the top floor to the printing room below street level. The poetical prose, so admired by Willich, went to the back pages in an occasional essay in Missouri wild flowers or family etiquette or the recollections of an Indian fighter. Crime news, accident news, political news moved to the front pages. A new reporter was hired and trained to write as Joseph wanted: short, factual sentences, what happened, where it happened, names and dates and places.

The public seemed to like the changes, but the two old partners thought he was going too far. They *knew* he was going too far when they found that his idea of political news was to print any story that came his way regardless of whether it reflected on the Democratic or Republican party, or whether or not it boosted the German community in St. Louis.

"He'll get us into trouble, Carl," Emil moaned. "I cannot even recognize our paper any more. The *Westliche Post* is not a dignified journal any more; it is a grab bag."

They bought Joseph out. He would have fought to stay except for one thing: he was alarmed for his health. He had worked

84

around the clock these last months. A doctor advised him that unless he took a rest he might develop serious lung trouble. Joseph doubted this but he was worried over his constant throbbing headaches caused by the increased strain to his overworked eyes.

His price was thirty thousand dollars.

At twenty-five years of age he was a rich man. Although he was dazed by it, the money had no meaning for him; rest and leisure were just words in somebody else's vocabulary. For years he had been running, running, running—hungry, eager, driven—and now, suddenly, there was no place to run to and no need to run.

He left St. Louis without even saying good-by to his friends. Not until he was halfway across the ocean, bound for his old home and his family, did Joseph begin to recover. The headaches left him. His health returned and with it full consciousness of his great good fortune.

In the old, familiar brick house in Budapest he was welcomed with tears and with love. Louise Politzer-Blau was beside herself with joy. "Look—I have to reach up now to box his ears; my Joseph is so tall!" And Joseph, man that he was at twenty-five, felt his face wet with tears. She was as unchanged to him, as beautiful, as loving as he had remembered her to be.

But the home was not as he had thought about it all these years. His stepfather was a good man but only a fair businessman. He had not earned thirty thousand dollars when he was only twenty-five years old! Max Blau was jealous and his jealousy made him doubt Joseph. "A police commissioner—a newspaper owner! Your Joseph is just bragging. The son wants the mamma to believe he is a big man in his America," he grumbled to his wife.

Albert, the younger brother, was torn between hero worship of Joseph and the fear that perhaps the stepfather was right. One moment he would follow his strange, foreign brother around the house like a shadow, trying to act just as Joseph acted, dreaming of becoming just what Joseph was; the next moment he would jeer at him in the same words as the stepfather.

The age difference between Joseph and Albert had widened too much. Albert had no experiences to match his older brother's. He listened with awe to the stories of America; they were hard to believe. "But I will come to see you in this city of St. Louis, yes? Please?" he begged.

On his return voyage Joseph had time to think. He made leisurely visits to New York and to Washington. Why did he feel at home here and such a stranger in Budapest?

He was completely, wholly, an American. Love for America had entered deep into the very core of his being. But why? Was it so different from other countries? There was evil in it as well as good. There were dishonest men, men whose god was the Almighty Dollar and who committed crimes in the name of that god. They held too much power. They stayed safely behind in the cities, while other men ran risks of death and danger to find the rich timberland of the West and the good bottomland for farming and the shining ore in the mountains and then, when the pioneers had staked their claims with a bit of string and a stick of wood and given that claim their strength and love, the Almighty Dollar came in and took it all away.

Why, then, did he love America so much? The answer was simple—because of the promise of freedom and equality. The nation had fought for that promise twice, once in the Revolution and again in the Civil War. The promise said there should be no princes, no serfs, no masters and no slaves; a man should have the right to his opinions, regardless of right or wrong. Could he have spent an evening in Budapest as he used to in Roslein's Bookstore in St. Louis, where every Friday night men gathered to talk and argue? English Chartists, French Socialists, German Marxists—all of them had come to America to find freedom of speech. He had heard hundreds of ideas put forth that would, in the opinion of this man or that, change the country for the better.

These ideas did not tempt him. Pulitzer was a reformer, not a changer. But he respected these men even if he didn't agree with them; they had come to America for the freedom to speak their minds. If they lost that freedom, then the America he loved would no longer exist.

Davidson met him at the St. Louis Depot on his arrival home. "You've been gone a long time," the schoolteacher grumbled as the two walked to the curb. He hailed a carriage driver. "What kept you? You wrote from New York you would be back in a week."

"I stayed longer in Washington than I expected to. It was—well, it was very pleasant there." Joseph turned his head away quickly. He picked up a big suitcase and began to stow away his luggage on the floor of the carriage. But he had not turned his head quickly enough; Davidson had seen the color rise in his face and the secretive smile that twisted the corner of his mouth.

What was the mystery? But before he could ask questions he heard Joseph say: "To the Lindell Hotel, driver." The taller, younger man leaped into the carriage and pulled Davidson in after him with a boyish energy that conflicted with the new maturity of his face and his body.

"The Lindell, lad?"

"That's right, Thomas. I've moved from Mrs. Augustus'. Koeppler stays at the Lindell and so do some of his friends. He has been trying for nearly a year to get me to move there." They were just passing a stable when Joseph yelled "Stop!" to the astonished carriage driver, leaped over the wheels while they were still moving and, with a quick "Be just a second!" ran into the stable.

In no time at all he was back. "Just wanted to see if they still had that brown mare for sale. They did, so I bought her." He settled back into the carriage and they drove off once again.

Davidson marveled. "New clothes—all these suitcases full of

them. You buy a horse, go to a new hotel—what has happened to you, Joseph?"

"I suddenly realized," Joseph answered, smiling broadly, "that I have some new lessons to learn. I have to find out how to enjoy myself. Do you know that since I was a child I haven't played or had fun? I've worked around the clock, day and night. Now it is time to discover some of the good things in life."

"Well, have your fun. You've earned it. But don't expect me to go roistering about with that crowd of Koeppler's."

Koeppler's friends, the gayest blades and the most fashionable young men of all St. Louis, with reputations for having considerable polish and culture and drawing-room sophistication, waited for Joseph that night in Koeppler's hotel room. They had planned dinner first, at the best restaurant, and then they were bound for the play at the Opera House.

None of them, except their host, knew Pulitzer well. They were worried because he had been invited.

"It's all right for you to be charitable, Arthur, because you are fond of the fellow, but think of the rest of us! We have no way of knowing how a newspaperman behaves in polite company—he is more used to police courtrooms and investigating murders in saloons," a banker's son fretted.

Arthur Koeppler told them: "You needn't worry. He has good manners."

"But he has bad politics, my good chap. He's a wild man, a radical. There's no getting away from that. I heard him make a speech. He was so intense he even *looked* wild. Couldn't we have introduced him to society in a small way first? I don't relish sitting in an opera box with everyone staring."

The door opened and they stopped talking. They watched Joseph Pulitzer walk into the room and four jaws dropped and four mouths widened in gaping surprise.

The man who had come in was a man transformed. The well-cut evening clothes showed a form that had finally matured and grown into the wide shoulders and the big bones. Joseph was still slender but it was the slenderness of strength and muscle; the black, satin-lined evening cloak hung on him with grace. But more than the physical appearance was the distinction with which he carried himself and the rugged nobility of his head. He gave the impression of imposing stature and intellectual power. Even the banker's son was impressed and he looked with envy at the style of the snowy white cravat and the white silk scarf, the fawn-colored gloves and the gold-topped cane, thinking to himself that it was these things that made the difference.

Koeppler exclaimed: "Joe, you're a darned handsome man!"

Pulitzer took a look at himself in the long, gilt-edge pier mirror. What was Koeppler talking about? The clothes were elegant, true—the product of New York's best tailors—but he was seeing the same big cheekbones, the same prominent nose, the high forehead of the immigrant boy and the army boy and the boy who had bummed rides on freight trains and had frozen and roasted that night on the St. Louis ferry. The beard, short, reddish and pointed in the Vandyke fashion, changed it somewhat and gave a balance to the face, but to him it was still the face that people made fun of. He shrugged with indifference. Did thirty thousand dollars in the bank make a man handsome?

He was wrong. What Koeppler saw, and what he himself could not recognize, was the character and strength and achievement written in his face that attracted like a magnet.

For several weeks he enjoyed all the fun that St. Louis had to offer. It was both unexpected and pleasant to find himself sought after, particularly by parents who wanted him to meet their daughters. He had become a very eligible young man for marriage. Every morning he exercised his brown mare, usually with a pretty girl riding at his side; every evening found him at a party, a dance or a dinner, and with a different female partner each night.

In the midst of all this he took a few days out to make another small fortune.

The *Staats-Zeitung*, a German newspaper, was about to fold up. Joseph heard about it; he also knew that it held that rare thing, an Associated Press franchise and that another paper, the Morning *Globe*, had just been launched, without this franchise. Joseph bought the *Staats-Zeitung* for practically nothing. Everyone thought he was crazy. He wasn't. He had no use for the *Staats-Zeitung*, but the day after he purchased it he sold the franchise to the Morning *Globe* for twenty thousand dollars. What little equipment there was left of the old *Staats-Zeitung* he let go to the sheriff for unpaid taxes.

Now the mammas and the papas not only had to respect him as a clever newspaperman but also as a clever businessman. He became a fine prospect, indeed. Invitations, handwritten and delicately scented, poured into his mailbox at the Lindell Hotel for teas and evening musicales.

They were a little upset when he took another small venture into politics. For a future son-in-law this young Pulitzer had such uncomfortable ideas!

He was a delegate to the Constitutional Convention called to revise the old Missouri Convention which had been passed in 1865, and as a delegate he was free to speak without ties to any political party. His biggest fight was for free public schools.

He also spoke against the trusts and monopolies which were placing a strangle hold on the free enterprise of the state:

I heartily despise demogogical appeals against the rich, or any particular class, but this question is so grave that it must be treated without gloves. The growth of the money power in this country has been fabulous, and its connections with and interest in the Government is alarming. We all want prosperity, but not at the expense of liberty. Poverty is not as great a danger to liberty as is wealth, its corrupting, demoralizing influences. Let us have prosperity, but never at the expense of liberty, never at the expense of real self-government, and let us never have a Government at Washington owing its retention to the power of the millionaires than to the will of the millions.

This statement was a formula Pulitzer was to hold to and fight for all the rest of his life.

Idleness was becoming unpleasant. He was restless. His friends advised all sorts of business ventures to occupy him and all sorts of entertainment to divert him. The mammas and papas increased their efforts to interest him in their daughters. When he suddenly announced that he had secured the position as special correspondent to Charles Dana's New York *Sun* everyone was delighted, but when he added that the position was *not* in St. Louis but in Washington, D.C. there was consternation. Why Washington? There were plenty of such correspondents' jobs in St. Louis.

Ever since his return Joseph had kept a secret. On his trip back from Europe he had stopped off in Washington and there he had met a girl. He had fallen in love. Only Thomas Davidson knew her name. He had pried the mystery out of his friend.

"Your Kate—you say she is bonny? As bonny as your lovely mother?" touching the miniature on Joseph's desk. Davidson had come to say good-by to his friend. "But does she love you, Joseph?"

Even to Davidson he disliked putting his most intimate thoughts into words. "I think so, though it hardly seems possible that she would choose me when she is so beautiful and accomplished and charming that half the men in Washington are after her to marry them. I only know I cannot find out if I'm in St. Louis and she is in Washington."

"And her family? Do they approve of their bairn being courted by you?"

Joseph looked up from his packing and his mouth hardened into a grim line. Then it relaxed. He smiled. "Her father is William Worthington Davis—don't you know how important that name is, you ignorant Missourian? He is first cousin to Jefferson Davis and tiptop society in Washington. I am competing with men who have so much money it makes my thousands look like peanuts. I've been elected to a backwoods state legislature; Kate has one suitor who is an ambassador. I ran a newspaper for a few months; Kate could have her pick among men who run million-dollar industries. But," he added, picking up a packet of letters written in a dainty feminine hand and bouncing them in the palm of his hand, his smile broadening to a big, boyish grin, "I think she likes me very much, Thomas. It's a miracle, but I think she does."

When he walked into the drawing room of the Davis home a fortnight later there was no further doubt in his mind. Kate saw him clear across the throng of other guests; the expression on her face, caught off guard, of frank delight and open warmth told him all he needed to know. She *was* beautiful. Her thick curls were piled on top of her head and caught there by a velvet band that was no more velvety than the smooth apricot of her cheeks or the smooth arch of her eyebrows. "I didn't expect you so soon, Mr. Pulitzer," she was saying, both hands caught in his, but her eyes were saying *why have you stayed away so long?*

The miracle was accomplished. Kate loved him.

It was not so easy to sell himself as a son-in-law to the Worthington Davises, however. They liked him but they did not approve of him. He had no great fortune, no family of standing in America, and—worse yet—no settled profession or career. Even though their questions were delicately stated, Joseph reacted with stiff and furious pride. He became haughty, even toward Kate. He would show them.

He qualified as a lawyer in Washington but this was only a

gesture. He had no intention of practicing law. Somewhere in the field of journalism there must be an opening he could find. He began a frantic search: one day he would hear of something in New York and run there—a prospect would open up in Baltimore and he would rush there—back to Washington for a few days—then off to New York again or Boston or Philadelphia or St. Louis.

All this might impress the parents but it was plain disturbing to Kate. It was certainly a most peculiar long-distance courtship and she didn't like it.

Her letter caught him, this time, in St. Louis. His answer was immediate:

St. Louis, Sunday noon, 1878

My dearest Kate:

What better answer can I make than this, that I shall return tomorrow evening? Have *you* not conquered, no? Yes.
... If you knew how much I thought of you these last days and how the thought of you creeps in and connects with every contemplation and plan about the present and future, you would believe it. I have an ideal of home and love and work—the yearning growing greater in proportion to the glimpse of its approaching realization. I am almost tired of this life—aimless, homeless, loveless, I would have said—but for you. I am impatient to turn over a new leaf and start a new life—one of which home must be the foundation, affection, ambition and occupation the cornerstones, and you, my dear, my inseparable companion. Would I were not so stupid always to be serious and speculative! Would I had your absolute faith and confidence instead of my philosophy! ...

There, now, you have my first love letter ... don't, of course, show my letters to anybody. I can't bear that thought. . . . .

Good-by till Wednesday.

J. P.

Kate, reading this, must have smiled. Her funny Joseph!—to worry about being "serious and speculative." This was just what she liked about him. Everything *mattered* to him more than to most people; he cared so deeply that his passion and intensity made him seem stern at times. She understood. And if her faith and confidence were what he needed then let there be no more nonsense about postponing the wedding. She didn't need the reassurance of his having a job to have faith in him.

They were married in the Episcopal Church of the Epiphany in Washington, in the same church where the bride's parents had been wed thirty years before.

They went to Europe for their honeymoon and were gloriously happy. Joseph discovered in Kate a companion such as he had never known. The people he had loved best before were serious, learned men like Davidson. It was a new experince to him to find, in Kate, both a firm mind and a frivolous one, a gift for making him laugh and at the same time a talent for listening to him and understanding him.

When they returned to St. Louis Joseph had no job and his money was dwindling fast. Kate was buoyantly optimistic. She laughed at his worries.

"Maybe you'll find another franchise to sell," she reminded him. The story of this coup had amused her; she thought her husband a very clever man for having thought of it.

This was an idea, so while Kate busied herself setting up housekeeping at 2929 Washington Avenue, buying as little furniture as possible in order not to put a further strain on their diminishing resources, Joseph "looked around" again. Immediately he saw a likely-looking venture. It was almost a duplicate of the *Staats-Zeitung* deal.

The newspaper was the St. Louis *Dispatch*. It was on the rocks with old, nearly worn-out equipment and a bank credit that was exhausted. It did have a building, a good one, and a press and type, but these latter two were in poor shape. The *Dispatch* was up for sale and its one advantage was its Associated Press franchise which Pulitzer had a strong hunch he could dispose of profitably to the St. Louis *Post,* which had none. He decided he could offer twenty-five hundred dollars for the *Dispatch* and agree to take over the thirty-thousand-dollar lien against it. If he sold the franchise to one bidder and the building to another he would certainly come out well ahead.

His was the only bid. The auction was held at the courthouse steps on the morning of December 9, 1878, and five minutes after the sale was announced and the auction opened, Pulitzer was the owner of another newspaper. Five minutes later three other excited bidders showed up but they were too late.

The sight of those other bidders made him thoughtful. Were they after the franchise, as he was, or was it actually possible they thought the *Dispatch* could be brought back to life as a functioning newspaper?

That day he steadfastly refused to go near his new possession. He didn't want to see it. There were several offers for the franchise and good offers, but for some reason he couldn't seem to make up his mind.

The next morning, with a strange, mixed feeling of reluctance, wariness and an unaccountable excitement, he went to look at the *Dispatch.* From the outside the building looked substantial. He fitted his key into the door and opened it. His eyes slowly adjusted to the gloomy darkness and what he saw appalled him. This was what he had bought sight unseen? Shabby, dirty walls, flimsy partitions knocked together any old way to mark off cubicles and rooms, windows unwashed, rickety chairs and tables—but these were not the worst. He waded through a solid pile of litter in the anteroom, past a disheveled mass of old papers, rags and torn blankets which had served as a bed under the staircase for tramp printers in exchange for a few days' work. He opened a grimy door

95

into the cement-floored, icy-cold room where the press was. At least it was a big and efficient-looking room!—but his heart sank as he looked at the press. It was in bad shape.

He heard footsteps overhead. He rang for the elevator and waited.

"Mr. Pulitzer?" a man's head appeared at the top of the stair well. "That elevator isn't working, sir. You'll have to walk up. I'm Briggs. I've been putting out the paper every day but I didn't know what you wanted to do about it."

Upstairs, the six men of the *Dispatch* staff crowded around him. They showed him the copy they had already put into type. He turned his face away from the pleading in their eyes; he knew what they were asking him.

"Go ahead. But just for this one day!" he said, brusquely.

He walked upstairs to the next floor, silently and sorrowfully cataloguing the repairs needed, the new equipment that would be necessary if—he caught himself up sharply. What could he be thinking about! He had bought this paper only to sell the franchise for the quick profit in it, nothing more.

By the time he was through with the tour of the top floor the forms of type were set up for the day's edition. He watched the staff pick up the forms and carefully, gently, carry them over to the stairs; one of the men got in front of the form to steady it and another two balanced it from behind.

"What do you think you're doing?" Pulitzer cried out, horrified.

The forms went bump-bump-bumping down the stairs. Briggs hastily explained. "It's the elevator, Mr. Pulitzer. It hasn't worked in a long time so this is the only way we can get the forms down to the printers."

This was too much. Pulitzer jammed his hat on his head and strode out. He poured all of his outrage out on Kate.

"It's indecent! A newspaper is like a living thing to me—how could they have let it get into such a shape as that? Like a child, a paper can get sick and maybe even die, but it shouldn't die in neglect, unwashed and dirty with nobody to look after it. Briggs feels the same way I do; he was ashamed to look at me; he was apologizing; he loved that paper and it sickens him to see it like that. But even he!—he could at least get a pail of water and soap and clean it up a little." One hand yanked at his tie, the other combed through his thick, wavy hair in angry frustration. An emotion had seized him that he could hardly explain.

Kate was puzzled. "But it's just a building, dear. You knew it was worn out or you couldn't have bought it for so little." Then a light came into her eyes. "Or is it just a building to you? Does it mean something more than that?"

"Of course not," he snapped. Then he apologized. "I'm sorry, Kate. I'm taking out my temper on you. Never mind. I'll see Dillon of the *Post* tomorrow and settle the deal—he can have the franchise *and* the building, if he wants it."

six

Dillon didn't wait for the next day. He came to see Joseph that night. For an hour the two men were closeted in the study and Kate could hear the murmur of their voices, cautious at first as two businessmen bargained over a price, then, suddenly, becoming animated. The two of them seemed to be excitedly talking at once as if they were making plans faster than the words could tumble out.

The editor of the *Post* was smiling as he came out, thanked his hostess, made his excuses for keeping her husband for so long a time and said his good nights. After he left, Kate turned to her husband.

"Well?"

"Well, what?"

"What is this all about? Why are you looking so pleased with yourself and so reckless, too?"

He seized her by the elbows and lifted her straight up into the air. While she squealed to be let down she was thinking this was a Joseph she had never seen before—jaunty, excited, with a flush in his cheeks kindled by a burning fire inside him. "I'm not selling— what do you think of that? I'm back in the newspaper business. How does this sound to you? The St. Louis *Post* and *Dispatch?*" (It was soon to be shortened and hyphenated.) "That's what it is, Kate. Dillon and I are going in on equal terms—his backlog of advertising and subscriptions and readers and my poor old building and equipment. He's been using the *Globe's* press to run his issues and it hasn't worked out too well. He's afraid I might run the *Dispatch* in competition with him, so he would rather merge even though it means I have complete control. That's why I am doing it! For the first time I will have a free hand and the final authority."

Kate had a momentary panic. There was exactly twenty-seven hundred dollars in the bank. How long would that last them, running a newspaper? But she looked at Joseph again and her confidence returned. He was a man transformed. Something that had been lying dormant in him for a while was awakened again and she knew that her husband was a newspaperman first and a businessman last. She quickly swallowed the words that might have dampened that fire and the eagerness she saw in his eyes.

"Come along, Editor Pulitzer—a glass of milk and a good night's sleep for you if you are going to put out a paper tomorrow."

"Kate," he promised fervently, "this is going to be a paper such as this city has never seen before!"

On the afternoon of the 12th the two papers officially merged. Everything that Dillon possessed was moved to the *Dispatch* building—a building that had been cleaned from top to bottom, scoured inside and out—and with a patched-up elevator that at least could *run*. Dillon had no money; they figured the Pulitzers' $2,700 would last them exactly seventeen weeks.

The new *Post-Dispatch* carried the following statement on its front page:

The *Post-Dispatch* will serve no party but the people; will be no organ of Republicanism, but the organ of truth; will follow no causes but its conclusions; will not support the "Administration" but criticize it; will oppose all frauds and shams wherever and whatever they are; will advocate principles and ideas rather than prejudices and partisanship.

These ideas and principles are precisely the same as those upon which our Government was originally founded, and to which we owe our country's marvelous growth and development. They are the same that made a Republic possible and without which a real Republic is impossible. They are the ideas of a true, genuine, real Democracy. They are the principles of true local self-government . . .

Joseph walked to the newly formed *Post-Dispatch* in the early dawn of the 12th. He was thinking hard. A statement published was one thing; living up to it would be another. He was going to have to strike fast, make a sharp impact, stir up the city within the next twenty-four hours—because people would be watching and waiting to see what he was going to do. A successful first edition would make the *Post-Dispatch,* but if he couldn't capture immediate attention then it would be a slow process of building readers. And twenty-seven hundred dollars in the bank wouldn't last that long.

It was a frightening prospect; but, oddly enough, Joseph was not the least bit frightened. He felt cocksure, happy, carefree—almost lighthearted. At last he had his own newspaper! Dillon would not interfere in any way, he knew.

Early as he was, Briggs had beaten him that morning and was already organizing the day's assignments. He turned a half-scared look at his new employer; then, seeing Pulitzer's smile, he beamed back. "So we're gonna have a paper, sir?"

"Looks that way, doesn't it? Well, we'll see—a lot will depend on today." But in spite of his efforts to be grave and serious, Joseph felt an intoxicating joy spreading inside of him. He wanted to shout and yell. Instead he took the notes and clippings Briggs handed him and quickly ran a practiced eye down them. "Hmmm—no lead story here. That's all right—don't worry about it. I have one and if we can do it, Briggs, it will be a spectacular story. It will jolt St. Louis right off its riverbanks. This is what I want you

100

to do." He wrote brief instructions and handed them to the reporter. Briggs read them and his eyebrows went up to a peak of astonishment. "Go over to the courthouse and don't come back until you have those figures. If you don't get them—if you make a mistake—well, maybe you'd just better not come back at all!" He made himself look severe.

Briggs scuttled out the door.

By the time the other reporter—from Dillon's staff—showed up, Joseph had all the rest of the day's news stories already arranged in his head; he had a pretty good picture of just what each page was going to look like. His training on the *Westliche Post*, even his frustrations there, had taught him to think not in terms of what was standard and usual and expected of newspapers, but rather what did the readers want? What would they like to read? What was missing that they did not get in the conservative press? And being something of a student of human nature, his journalistic sense led him to believe that he should make a real break with the kind of writing in the other papers.

"We're going to give our readers all the news—news they won't get anywhere else," Pulitzer explained to the reporter. "But the readers don't want just serious writing. We are going to give them color and drama and excitement, pictures, cartoons—lots of small, odd stories—lots of names in the stories—for instance, here's a clipping, one paragraph, from the *Democrat*. A girl says she met the Devil himself, in a country lane north of the city. The *Democrat* runs a paragraph only because the encounter frightened her so much that she became unconscious. But they've missed it as a story. Of course she didn't really meet any devil, but she thought so. It's a curiosity; it makes people wonder; makes them laugh, perhaps. I want you to interview her. She's at the Neighborhood Hospital. Write it with all the emotions she felt. *Something* scared her enough to make her faint. Get all these other stories"—indicating the assignments—"but concentrate on that girl. And I want *her* words, not yours."

The reporter, with a look that plainly said he thought his new employer was as crazy as a girl who saw devils, walked leisurely away.

Dillon put his head in the door. "I'll be out looking for advertisements. Not that I expect to get any." Both men knew that whatever success he would have in the advertising department would depend on how the public would like Joseph as an editor.

The printer yelled from downstairs. Joseph took the stairs three at a time, forgetting the elevator was now in working order. The press had developed new mechanical trouble, the printer told him with melancholy pride. It took them both an hour to find the trouble and repair it.

He raced upstairs again. The dispatches from the Associated Press had come in. There were four good stories: one of a new silver mine discovered in Nevada; one of a tremendous hurricane in the Samoan Islands; one of a great and glittering reception and ball in the White House, another of a fire in the Chicago packing sheds. Fairly routine stories—but Joseph had an idea. At lunch he went without food to find Arthur Koeppler and persuade him to draw a big picture, from his own imagination, of the White House ball. Koeppler had a fine way of drawing a crowd of people, yet the ones in the foreground had such distinction of face and figure that anyone could see they represented the President, his wife, and members of the Cabinet. Joseph decided, when he saw the quick sketch, to do a truly daring thing—he pulled out several stories to give space to splash the picture right across the third page.

The reporter was back with his interview from the hospital. He watched with fascination as Joseph completely rewrote it.

"Mr. Pulitzer! Your language—" he protested. His mouth was pinched in disdain. "That is hardly good journalism. It isn't in good taste. It's—it's *sensationalism!*"

102

Joseph looked hard at him. "You are absolutely right. That is what the *Post-Dispatch* will have, among other things. Sensation! Excitement! Now this is what I call a good story of its kind: Girl Meets Devil. Dark Lane. Dark Night. Suddenly the moon breaks through and she sees an awesome figure—she screams—"

"It is a ridiculous story. Making a lot out of nothing."

"The girl believes it. She saw something and she *did* faint and she *is* in the hospital. Maybe she has a dull life and just created some excitement for herself. Well, maybe our readers have dull lives, too. And if you feel this is beneath your literary dignity, I think you had better take yourself to another newspaper, because the St. Louis *Post-Dispatch* is going to amuse and entertain its readers as well as educate and instruct them."

The day wasn't half over and he had already fired one man. If Briggs didn't get back soon—no—there wouldn't be much point in firing him because there wouldn't be any newspaper from which to fire him. For a moment Joseph itched to be out of this editor's chair and into the streets, running along them as he used to do—getting the story, getting the facts—and getting them first.

Joseph felt that old, familiar twitching spasm of his nerves at the back of his neck. He rubbed his forehead. Nothing could go wrong today! It just couldn't!

The door opened. He swung around. But it was Kate, not Briggs. She had a basket with her and a white napkin over it. "You didn't come for me at lunchtime and I am sure you haven't eaten. Now, I am going to close this door and no one is to interrupt us. You are going to rest for a few moments while we eat."

His nerves relaxed. The happy feeling came flooding back and he smiled at her. Nothing could go wrong. He felt it as surely as he saw Kate herself bustling about, pushing papers aside on his desk to make it into a table. "Bless you, Kate. I'm waiting for a reporter and if he doesn't show up pretty soon with the story I sent him for, I am afraid our goose will be cooked."

"You say that as if you didn't really believe it could happen."

"I don't. If Briggs doesn't show up in half an hour I'll go myself."

"It's that important? Now, no more business talk. While you have been so busy here this morning I have found us a house to live in. Very nice, Joseph, and there's a stable near by where you can keep your horse and—oh, yes, I finally persuaded your friend Mr. Davidson to stop being shy of me and come for dinner next Sunday—" Kate rambled on and for twenty minutes Joseph completely forgot about Briggs and the missing story.

It was Briggs himself, hot, tired and panting, almost falling headlong into the room, who interrupted them before ten minutes had gone by.

"Did you get them?" Joseph demanded.

"I did." The reporter caught his breath. "Are you really going to print them, Mr. Pulitzer? They're dynamite!"

They were the city tax reports and they certainly were dynamite. The *Post-Dispatch* ran them, two columns wide: in one, the taxes paid by rich men, corporations and businesses; in the other, the taxes paid by workingmen and small businessmen. The contrast was shocking. Those in the first column had paid only a fraction of their assessments, using every kind of tax dodge. Those in the second, since they had no smart lawyers to advise them, and could not hire bookkeepers to juggle accounts, had paid their full tithes.

That first day Joseph wrote no editorial. He wanted his readers to judge for themselves.

The new St. Louis *Post-Dispatch* hit the streets for the first time late that afternoon. In a few hours it was completely sold out. By evening there were people at the newspaper doors demanding extra copies; the best Pulitzer could do for them was to paste up one of the office file copies on the windows where it could be read by the crowd in the street.

This had its advantages. He could stand out there with them, unnoticed, and watch their reactions.

By twentieth century standards that first issue of the *Post-Dispatch* would be considered a very poor journalistic effort. The press was so old and worn out that the type smeared in some places and was so faint as to be barely readable in others. There were no headlines, story leaders were small and the copy was jammed up against them with hardly two spaces between them. Lead, sublead and the story itself were of the same gray-black type, with no white spaces or blacker type to break the monotonous pattern.

But in 1878 the Pulitzer paper was a radical change from anything those crowds on the sidewalk had ever seen. It had *news!* The tax story was indeed dynamite. No other paper would have touched it. Two columns of that on the front page, next to them the Samoan hurricane, a fourth column of short stories of local interest, and the last column an account of the Chicago packing sheds fire. The style of the writing was different, too: right to the point, easy to read.

Pulitzer stood quietly by the window, pretending to read but actually listening to the comments.

"Just look at that! Those dirty crooks, cheating the city while we pays up honestly!"

"That's Edgerton's name, printed right there. Five hundred dollars for two of the biggest department stores is all he paid last year! Now, you know that's a swindle.... There's my cousin's name— right there in the next column—you know my cousin? the one lives on Chestnut Street? Well, whattya know! Bet that's the first time he ever got his name in a paper."

"It can't be true—"

"Why can't it? You think a newspaper's gonna print something they can't back up?"

"You don't know what you're saying. All newspapers lie all the time."

"Not with figures they don't. It says these are *official* tax reports and we can go down and check them ourselves."

The crowd swelled. People read over each other's shoulders. They exclaimed, they argued, they grew heated and angry; they moved down the sidewalk to examine the other pages and to linger, especially, over the Koeppler drawing of the White House ball. Pictures were extremely rare in newspapers. They were considered fit only for magazines.

One comment Pulitzer heard over and over again. He could hardly wait to rush home and tell Kate.

"They kept saying 'tomorrow I'm going to buy a paper for myself. I want the wife to read this.' And tomorrow, Kate, it's going to be a better paper. I have more tax lists to run; there will be an editorial on it. I wish Koeppler weren't going to New York. We'll have to find another illustrator. Dillon is worried. We didn't have a single advertisement but I told him not to be upset. They may try to boycott us for a little while because of this tax story, but if the subscriptions go up the advertisers will follow. If we get the readers —their customers—they will come to us, eventually. I must see Briggs—"

"Joseph," she said, "calm yourself. You are speaking so fast I can hardly follow you. Dinner is ready."

"No dinner." He kissed her quickly, seized his broad-brimmed felt hat and slipped his arms into his heavy topcoat. "I must get back; there's a whole night's work waiting for me." And he was gone.

He worked until midnight and the next morning he was the first to open the *Post-Dispatch* doors. He took a chance. This day's issue, featuring more of the tax records and a Mississippi steamboat disaster, was a double run off the press. Even with that increase, it was almost sold out by six o'clock.

Pulitzer's judgment had been sound on the story of the girl's encounter with the Devil. It became a topic of gossip and controversy. Letters came in the mail—denouncing it as superstition, treating it as a joke, arguing about it from every possible angle. Joseph printed the letters without comment and let the readers argue it out among themselves. With this one single stroke, the *Post-Dispatch* was established as a newspaper that belonged not solely to its publisher but to the readers themselves as well.

He hired a new reporter, trained him to write dramatically and taught him to go out and hunt for stories in the same way the young Joseph Pulitzer had done for the old *Westliche Post*—with this difference: this reporter knew his stories would not be censored for any political, religious or financial allegiance of the publisher's.

Dillon still worried. The advertisers stayed away.

Gambling and vice in St. Louis were Joseph's next targets. He kept Briggs busy from morning until night collecting facts for this exposé. Pulitzer found another artist and he edged close to libel suits when the drawings featured, unmistakably, the faces of well-known gambling figures. In a couple of weeks the *Post-Dispatch* had literally run the St. Louis Lottery Company out of town and won the gratitude of families who had seen husbands spend the grocery money on the faro tables or in a thousand-to-one shot on a lottery ticket.

Editorially, Pulitzer followed the gambling stories with outright attacks on the city government, on real estate companies, on the lottery outfit itself—anyone who was in any way involved in permitting gambling to flourish in the city.

That campaign finished, he turned to a demand that the city streets be cleaned and repaired. Many were nothing but hog wallows. His articles, also, were responsible for the beginning of a park system in St. Louis.

Because of Schurz's training, he knew his way around in the political field. His experiences in the legislature gave him an inside knowledge that he could now freely pass on to his readers. He held nothing back from them. Only in the editorial did he state his own opinions.

Long, long before the twenty-seven hundred dollars in the bank was supposed to have been exhausted the newspaper was on its own and making money. Circulation climbed every week. With the tax scandal out of its pages, the advertisers forgot their boycott. As Pultzer had predicted, they would put aside their grudge to reach their customers.

Dillon was amazed at their overnight success. To him it seemed a miracle of genius or an accident of fortune. Pulitzer knew it was neither accident nor miracle. It was the result of hard work. In spite of the happiness that was truly his at that time, with the *Post-Dispatch* leaping into journalistic and financial success overnight, with the fun of setting up housekeeping with Kate and with the pleasure of introducing old friends to his wife and making new ones through her, there was another side to the picture. The *Post-Dispatch* succeeded only because its editor risked both his health in long hours of hard work and risked his safety for his principles.

There was the terrible night when Kate, expecting him home early for once, waited supper for him. The minutes dragged on and then the hours and still he did not come. Three times she sent the cold dishes back from the table to the kitchen to be reheated. It was not unusual for him to be late—but not this late. Somehow she had a premonition of danger. She was afraid. Her face was pale and drawn when finally she heard his steps on the porch.

The steps didn't sound like Joseph's. They faltered and stumbled. Kate raced to fling open the door and then she screamed.

"Joseph!—oh, you're hurt—!" Blood from his clothes had come off on her hands. He staggered a little and supported himself by clinging to her with one hand, the other clutching for support at the prong from the big walnut hatrack in the hallway. He managed to smile at her.

"It's all right. Now, don't fuss, Kate—"

108

"All right? How can you say that? Mary, run for the doctor, please! Bring me a towel first and some hot water. Joseph, tell me what happened. Who did it?" She guided him to the dining room and to a chair. He sank into it with a sigh that hurt her more than the sight of the bleeding wound on his head and neck.

"It was the gambling syndicate. I don't know whether they sent this man or he did it on his own, but I recognized him. He hangs around one of the worst gambling dens in the city and picks up odd jobs for them. He came up behind me. The street was dark and I didn't see or hear him until he was right on top of me with his club. I finally—ouch, Kate!—that stings—finally managed to get it away from him—and just then a policeman ran up. He had his hands full with my would-be assassin. I couldn't find a hackney to drive me so I just walked on home. Guess I didn't realize I was hurt until my knees began to give way." He closed his eyes. He opened them, quickly, to reassure her. "It isn't serious, dear. The doctor will fix me up."

As soon as his head was bandaged he insisted on driving back with the doctor to the police station. It was no longer a personal attack on him; it was a story for the *Post-Dispatch*. Not even Kate's tears could keep him home.

He never told her that two weeks before he had been set upon in broad daylight in the busiest street of the city by a Colonel W. B. Hyde, editor of the *Republican*, for what the man thought was a slur on his paper's integrity. It had been easy to disarm the colonel of his cane, and without it he became suddenly very prudent and peaceful. Pulitzer went on his way without another thought of the incident.

Although a lesser woman than Kate Pulitzer might have begged her husband to give up the crusading that got him into so much trouble, a lesser woman would probably not have married someone as intensely perfectionist and as boldly idealistic as Joseph.

She worried mostly about his health.

109

All that year and for several to come, he was to work like a man possessed. There were only a few little concessions she could win from him: a Sunday nap once in a while, an early-morning ride, an infrequent evening of leisure at home with guests. Most of the time he worked from early in the morning until late at night. Sometimes he was the first to open the doors of the *Post-Dispatch* and usually the last to leave at night. At times he slept there, on an old horsehair couch. He worked with an intensity that was frightening to his staff and at the same time reassuring to them. Nothing could go wrong as long as Pulitzer was there, they felt. If a mistake was made he was sure to catch it. If a man needed help, the tall, distinguished figure of the editor was at his side, rewriting a story, proofreading, and in an emergency he could even set type or help with the patched-up, creaky old press.

On the other hand, none of the staff knew what to expect next. The pace he set them was killing. He added reporters to the pay roll; trained as they were to the ways of other editors, it seemed to them that Pulitzer's intent was to shake every old habit and method and routine out of them. They were sent scurrying to every corner of St. Louis in search of stories. They were made to force their way into offices and buildings and homes and churches and schools and city institutions with no respect for anything except to *get the story! get the facts!* "It's ungentlemanly," one complained to another. "It's undignified." "It'll make a reporter out of you," Briggs retorted with satisfaction.

Lunch for the editor was a sandwich eaten while he worked, but if his hours kept him late, as they usually did, Kate would come to the office with her supper basket and insist that the two spend a quiet half hour eating and talking and relaxing together. She knew very well that this was often the only moment in the whole day that he could take to rest. And because she saw so little of him she would repack the basket when they finished, take her mending or her embroidery over to her favorite corner of his office

110

and work quietly until Joseph was ready to leave. Though he argued with her about the trouble she was taking for him, he loved to feel her presence there even when he was so busy he scarcely saw her.

There were days when he wrote virtually the entire paper himself. It was slow work changing the style of his new reporters from pretty prose to hard-hitting, colorful, crisp language. It was even slower work to convince them they need fear no one; pay favors to no one regardless of how rich or prominent he might be. The pace was too fast for Dillon. At the end of the first year he was glad to sell Joseph his share and be rid of responsibility. Now the entire burden of publisher and editor fell on one man. It was too much. He looked around for an able assistant and found him in John A. Cockerill.

Cockerill was called "Colonel" but he laughed at the title, saying that since the Civil War everyone who had had a sniff of battle gave himself brass and rank and that he had been nothing but a drummer boy himself. But his friends insisted on the "Colonel" because his father had been one.

He was as stormy a man as his boss and he kept both of them in hot water. His history had been adventurous: after his army days he had been a printer's devil, then a clerk in the state senate of Ohio, then a reporter for the Dayton, Ohio, *Empire*. He had gone to the battle front of the Russo-Turkish War as a special correspondent for the Cincinnati *Enquirer*. When Pulitzer first heard of him he was managing editor of the Baltimore *Gazette*, a battling, two-fisted, picturesque character.

It was Cockerill, more so than Pulitzer, who fully developed the style of terse, rapid, short-sentence news reporting. Just as his boss was master of the editorial, he was a master of the front page.

Kate liked him; more than that, she was glad that someone was to share part of her husband's load.

"I'm so worried about Joseph, Thomas," she told Davidson one

111

quiet night when they finished dinner and Joseph had gone back to the paper. "He has driven himself past that point of weariness where the body can recover with a few good nights' rest. He is exhausted and yet the nervous tension in him won't give up, won't stop.

"He has always been that way, although this is worse than I have ever seen. We must try to make him take a vacation. His eyes are growing weaker with this constant reading of proof and copy. He abuses those poor eyes of his."

She looked up over her sewing. "It is his nervousness that alarms me most," she continued. "He jumps at every sudden sound. He can hardly sleep. He has developed a habit of rubbing his forehead as if he could make the pain and the headache go away, and it hurts me every time I see him do it. Perhaps Mr. Cockerill can take complete charge for a while and we can have our vacation—the paper is doing very well, isn't it, Thomas?"

" 'Well,' lassie? It is a spectacular success! When I think of Joseph as I first met him, it's hard to realize that today he owns one of the biggest newspapers in the city and is himself a highly respected—aye, and a feared mon, too! But I did not come here to talk of the big father. I came to see the bairn."

She laughed. "Ralph is in bed at this hour. Babies sleep, you know. But we can go up and peek at him. I think you are almost as proud of Ralph as Joseph is!"

It was too soon for the vacation they hoped for. Another year and another. Still the *Post-Dispatch* swallowed up almost every minute of Pulitzer and Cockerill's time and effort. The two men slaved. They hired more reporters, added another bookkeeper, and a business manager named McGuffin who proved to be a wonder at bringing in advertising. More advertising meant more pages; more pages meant more work, more stories. A new press must be bought and a new building to house the bigger and completely up-to-date equipment. On December 21, 1881, they moved to 517 Market Street and added still another Hoe press.

Now the *Post-Dispatch* had come into its own as the leading newspaper of St. Louis. Competitors were slowly beginning to copy its style of writing and even—though they still denounced it—some of its sensationalism.

Now it was time for Kate to insist that Joseph take a rest. There were three babies now—little Ralph was three years old, Lucille Irma two and Katherine Ethel an infant in the cradle. It was time for their father to really get acquainted with his children, Kate insisted. Joseph loved his children but he was missing so much of their childhood by being so busy. He was missing that real closeness of a father to a son, and he had better start answering some of Lucille Irma's questions, because that young lady, at two years of age, was just like him. She was into everything, curious about everything, asking questions about everything.

It was time. The paper was prospering. In Cockerill's hands it could be taken for granted that it would continue to do so. This last year had shown a profit of eighty-five thousand dollars—but what good was this if Joseph's health should be permanently wrecked and if he was too busy to enjoy his family? He agreed. By the fall of 1882 he had put his affairs in such shape they could make their plans to winter in California.

Then—disaster.

On October 5th a man named Colonel Alonzo W. Slayback, of the law firm of Broadhead, Slayback and Haeussler, was shot and killed by Cockerill. The shooting took place in the editor's office in full view of Slayback's companion, a Mr. William H. Clopton. The composing room foreman happened to be passing and saw a little of what happened. Yet the versions of the shooting were startlingly different.

Clopton claimed that, while it was true Slayback rushed in through the office door at Cockerill, the slain man was trying to take off his coat for a fist fight and Cockerill had shot him down, in cold blood.

"What did happen, John?" Pulitzer asked. Cockerill had been released without bail and the two were alone in the publisher's office.

The editor was badly shaken but his eyes were steady as he faced his employer and his friend. "He came at me with a gun. It was in his hand, Joe, and he was pointing it at me as he ran into the room—Clopton was behind him, too far behind to see what was in his hand. There wasn't time to think. I just acted—reached into my desk drawer, grabbed my revolver and shot. It was self-defense."

"I believe you." Pulitzer's fingers pressed his throbbing temples. "Broadhead was one of Slayback's partners and we've been opposing Broadhead's candidacy for Congress. He knew that it was you who dug up the story that Broadhead had accepted a retainer of ten thousand from the city to fight a suit against the Laclede Gas Company and then, when he had learned all he needed to know about the city's case for the prosecution, turned around and defended the gas company against the city. That was a fine story you found. I had already heard rumors that Slayback was bragging all over the coffeehouses that he was going to 'have it out' with you."

"He sent word a day ago that he was challenging me to a duel. I'm sorry I killed the man but I don't know what else I could have done."

Pulitzer was remembering his own shooting fray of some years ago. "I'll stand by you, John. We'll weather this storm. The vacation trip will have to wait."

The storm, however, became a hurricane that threatened to wipe out both men and the *Post-Dispatch*, too. It was whipped into frenzy by the enemies the paper had made for itself.

The coroner's jury was satisfied with Cockerill's version. Since this was a duel between two individuals they did not trouble to

114

indict. It was still an age when guns were considered the proper weapon for men to adjust their differences.

But Pulitzer's enemies called it murder. They screamed that a man had been shot down, defenseless and helpless, in cold blood. Ward politicians went around their districts inflaming people; saloonkeepers, smarting under the *Post-Dispatch* crusade against vice and gambling, set up free drinks on the house for anyone who would go out and "get" Joseph Pulitzer. Rival editors wrote stories that were incitements to mob violence. As the day went on, the whirlwind became a fury and drove an ever-increasing horde of people to the doors of the newspaper.

From his third floor window Joseph watched the crowd gather. He heard the first isolated yells of "Murderer," the first calls to burn and lynch, and then he saw the whole crowd turn into a screaming mass milling around the doors, brandishing clubs and flaming pitch pine torches. It was a sight that burned itself into his brain. Beside him stood Kate. She had refused to leave. Her place was with him.

It was a hideous and desperate night. Windows were broken. Torches were thrown through them and Joseph and several of the staff—who had stoutly refused to leave—were kept busy putting out the flames before they could seriously burn floor or walls. Someone in the crowd brought up a battering-ram. Joseph could hear the furious noise of it pounding on the front door.

Extra police were finally called out and at last they were able to control the situation, confiscate the battering-ram and put out the torches. As the night grew cold so did the fury of the mob. They began to scatter, then the whole crowd broke up and ran.

At last the vigil upstairs was ended. Pulitzer drew the shades and turned away from the window. Kate caught her breath at the sight of his face. It was gray, heartsick and hurt.

The next day the edition of the *Post-Dispatch* came back almost completely unsold. Circulation dropped to zero.

"I don't understand it. The drunken mob, yes; I can understand

115

what was motivating them and who was behind them. But after all the paper has meant to the people of St. Louis that they should turn against me now!" The sickness was still in Pulitzer's face. "Why don't they trust our story, John, instead of others'?"

"Because they *are* decent, good people. That is what you don't realize. You think they should be personally loyal to you or to me, but to them murder is wrong no matter who does it. Yes—I know—it was self-defense. But the West is changing, Joe. They are demanding law, not guns, to settle disputes. The worst thing that happened was the coroner's jury court refusing to arrest me. If I had gone to trial and cleared myself, then it would have been all right. But this way it looks as if I took the law into my own hands and now the court is hushing things up for us. Joe, I know you aren't going to want to do this but you will have to let me resign. For the good of the *Post-Dispatch*."

Pulitzer held out for a while but he was forced to admit Cockerill was right. He had to replace him. Immediately sales and circulation began its upward swing and soon the *Post-Dispatch* was at the top of its field again.

But for Joseph Pulitzer the paper had a taint on it. It was spoiled. Even the city of St. Louis seemed to him now a treacherous and unfriendly place. With Dillon, his old partner, back as managing editor, he and Kate and the children were ready to leave for a vacation—but Joseph knew in his heart it was not really a vacation. He never wanted to come back.

"We'll work together again sometime, John," he told Cockerill. "You are still on the pay roll. If you find another position let me know, because I have a feeling I'll be needing you again."

"Don't worry about me. Kate tells me you are going to New York and then to Europe. Enjoy yourself. Rest. Take it easy. And don't think about work for a long, long time!"

"I won't. I don't even want to *read* a newspaper." He said it with violence.

seven

The New York of 1883 was very different from the city Pulitzer had first seen nineteen years ago. It had grown up, just as he had. Its shops and residential districts now spread out almost all over Manhattan Island; its skyline was rising, in some places as high as eight stories. Paving had replaced many of the old cobblestoned streets and the passengers of the horse-drawn streetcars welcomed the change. No longer did they jounce over ruts and stones and risk their necks when the wheels came off over a boulder or a horse fell down in the ice of a rut.

But if anything, the noise and the crowds and the rushing-about had increased. Kate, seeing New York for the first time, was breathless and confused. She had never seen so many people! Or heard so many different languages. "It's like a world all in itself," she said. "Some of the richest people in the world—and some of the poorest. Great mansions and terrible slums. The finest stores—and on the same street women with shawls over their heads selling shoelaces from pushcarts. And the noise!—steamship whistles and fire engine bells and—look, Joseph!—did you ever see so many vehicles on one street in your life?" She leaned out the window of their suite in the Fifth Avenue Hotel, clutching her husband's arm to steady herself.

Joseph counted them off for her: "Two broughams, a carriage, a chaise, the horse-drawn tram, brewery wagon, two hackney cabs, a coach, a hire-carriage—that's ours and it's waiting for us. You wanted to see the Bowery, Kate."

"Is it really dangerous?"

"Not if we are in a carriage. But it is a tough place. The choicest collection of pickpockets and thieves and murderers you could find outside of a jail or San Francisco's Barbary Coast."

The mornings were devoted to playing games with the children. For Joseph it was an adventure, finding out how intelligent his little son was, yet how different was the child's personality from his own. Lucille Irma not only acted like her father, she looked most like him; both children were enchanted to have this big man all to themselves for once. He was gentle with them; they climbed on his lap and pulled his beard and he only laughed at their baby tempers. "You'll spoil them if you aren't careful," Kate warned, rocking little Katherine in her cradle. Secretly she didn't care. For her, it was enough to have her husband and her family together in one room.

They had brought a nurse with them. While the children napped in the afternoons they could be left in her care. Kate and Joseph went sight-seeing, shopping and visiting.

One of the first persons they visited was Albert. Joseph's younger brother had come to America some years before. He had come directly to St. Louis but while he was there the separation between the brothers that had started in Budapest widened to a definite cool estrangement. There were all sorts of rumors, but whatever the reason, Albert left St. Louis and came to New York.

He, too, was interested in journalism. He had proved himself a highly competent reporter for the New York *Herald* and only the year before this one, with Joseph's financial help, he had branched out on his own and bought the *Morning Journal,* a one-cent newspaper, for twenty-five thousand dollars.

Perhaps Joseph felt that one newspaperman in the family was enough. Perhaps he disliked being imitated. He showed little faith

118

in the *Morning Journal*—though it was already a mild success—and when the two met in New York they were friendly, but scarcely warm.

This and the continuing worry over Joseph's health were the only clouds in their lives. Kate went with him to consult the best physicians. The verdict only confirmed her own diagnosis: complete rest and absence from the strain of work. One doctor, however, showed an insight the others did not.

"Ordinarily, Mrs. Pulitzer, for a patient whose nerves are in such bad shape I would prescribe bed rest. That would be the worst thing in this case. Your husband has an extremely active mind and boredom would be as much of a strain on him as overwork. I would suggest you find diversion for him that will not tax his strength but at the same time will provide him mental activity."

She knew this was sound advice but she was at her wit's end to provide the diversion. Shopping in the fine New York stores was fun, but only for a little while; sight-seeing was mainly for her since Joseph was no stranger to this city. He was enjoying the hours he could now spend with his children, getting really acquainted with them, but babies hardly provided the kind of mental stimulation the doctor had suggested. Only one idea came to her mind.

Kate began to entertain. She sought out old friends of her parents and mingled them with some of Joseph's acquaintances as supper guests in the hotel suite. She was a charming hostess. Her husband's history made him a fascinating and exciting figure. Invitations poured in on them; she accepted them recklessly.

Joseph was surprised. "I didn't expect my wife to turn out to be a social butterfly."

"You enjoy it," she defended herself. "And it is only for one more week. It is nice to hear people talk of something else besides Missouri politics and Missouri problems. Don't you think so, dear?"

"It's more than just nice and pleasant, Kate. It's like a big, strong, fresh wind blowing through my mind. In St. Louis it was hard to interest more than a handful of people in anything happening outside the city or state, but these friends of yours from Washington are talking about national and international politics." He tugged at the vest and picked up his tie. They were dressing to go out for dinner. "Help me with this, will you?"

She stood on tiptoe to fix his tie. "I am so glad that all that desk work has never made you stoop shouldered. And I like that vest." It was flowered brocade, on a dull and sedate background. Kate was even more pleased at the eager spark that had come back into Joseph's eyes. He was sleeping well now; the headaches were less frequent; his face was animated.

"Don't you know what the New York *Sun* said of me?—a *distinguished visitor.* Since they went on to deplore the 'sensationalism' of my journalistic endeavors, it can't be that they are referring to. It must be my looks," he teased her. "But, to get back to your friends, do you mind that I argue with them so much? Does it spoil your evenings, Kate? There is a presidential election coming up and I am convinced that if a good candidate can be found, the saving of this country will be through a Democratic party victory. Under both Grant and Arthur this country has absolutely been plundered of its richest natural resources—" he was beginning to pace the floor, forgetting the clock and his unfinished dressing. "Railroad barons, particularly. The gold and silver and oil and steel companies—just as bad. They've grabbed off the cream and left the skim for the people! And very little skim at that. So I argue with our Republican friends and try to convince our Democratic ones. Unfortunately, the Democrats aren't convinced they can win. They aren't thinking big enough. They aren't looking for the kind of man who is a strong man, a good man—and one who could win!"

"But people *do* listen to you. Hurry, dear! Put on your coat—do

120

you like my new dress? Aren't these bustles the silliest things? They wear so many more puffs and pads here than I am used to—and I am bound I'll trip myself on this train." She kicked the green satin folds aside. He held her fur-trimmed cloak for her.

She was thoughtful as they walked to the street. "People do listen to you," she repeated. "Last night Mr. Montague said to me: 'Your husband is a powerful man, Mrs. Pulitzer. He owns a powerful newspaper in the Middle West and thousands and thousands of people will vote as he tells them to.' This is true, Joseph. I never thought of your having so much influence on a national election."

"It may be true," he admitted gloomily, "but it is New York that still casts the deciding vote. The voice that controls the country is right here, not in Washington and certainly not in St. Louis. Also, these next few months will settle who is going to be the candidate and I will be in Europe during those months."

Only one more week and they would be on the boat for Europe, Kate thought, and then we will really be on holiday. One more week and I will have him to myself.

Nothing could be allowed to spoil this vacation!

On Thursday they had a luncheon engagement with another couple at Rector's Restaurant and planned to visit a museum afterward. Kate was dressed and ready and waiting for Joseph who had gone out early that morning. The noon hour came closer. Still no Joseph. A messenger arrived with a note: "Please go on without me. I am detained on business. Will explain later. J. P." She wondered but went on, expecting to find him at Rector's. No Joseph. She was becoming provoked and a little worried. Her friends persuaded her to eat. When he still had not shown up by two o'clock she refused to go with them to the museum. She went back to the hotel rooms to wait.

The dinner hour brought another message: "Forgive me but am still busy. Make my apologies to the Andersons. Will be home late."

121

She sent the messenger on to the Andersons to make both their excuses. Kate was not budging from those rooms until she found out what the mystery was. Her fears mounted with each passing hour.

When Joseph came in, one look at his face confirmed those fears. The relaxed sparkle was gone. In its place was the determination, the absorption, the settled purpose and willfulness she had so dreaded in the past few years.

"Tell me what has happened! What is this—this business—that kept you?"

"Kate, I am sorry." In his hands were a ledger book and a thick sheaf of foolscap, which was closely covered with scribbles of figures and notes. He placed them carefully on the round mahogany table and stood looking at them, absent-mindedly, as he spoke. "I am afraid I have bad news for you. We will have to postpone our vacation."

"Why?"

"I am considering buying another newspaper."

She sank down on a chair, stunned. "I don't understand. Why?"

"Because I want a New York newspaper. You know I am not too much interested in making more money; the *Post-Dispatch* does very well for us and I might even lose everything in a venture like this. But I want a voice that will speak not only to one city but to the whole nation, and only the New York press does that. I want to have a hand in deciding who will be the next president. I want to help shape the future of this nation. I want to tell people facts and truth and show both the politicians and the other newspaper publishers what a tremendous instrument for the public good a newspaper—our kind of a newspaper—can be."

She realized he had been carefully formulating and marshaling these arguments before he would see her.

"But, dear, you are tired. You are not well. Can't this wait until we return from Europe?"

"I thought so. But you have to seize an opportunity when it comes along or you might not get another. Wedging yourself into the New York field is almost impossible under most circumstances; the press here is established and it's big and it wants no newcomers butting in. I heard today that Jay Gould wanted to sell the *World*. It is a small paper; used to be a religious one, then Gould got hold of it and used it to boost his financial interests. It is a Democratic paper and has a few stanch subscribers—that's all. But the equipment," he said indicating the papers on the table, "is the best. The price is three hundred and forty-six thousand dollars and while that is not exactly a bargain it is a price I can meet. I have to do this, Kate! I may never have such a chance again."

She was speechless. He watched her face but he could not read it.

"I spoke to Albert about it," he went on. "Albert's opinion is that there isn't room in this city for two Pulitzers—or for another paper such as I have in mind—to compete with the biggest—the *Times*, the *Herald*, the *Sun*—"

That was the worst thing Albert could have said, she thought to herself, despairingly. Opposition only made Joseph more determined than ever, if it was the kind that implied he would fail. It acted on him like a dare.

"But I'm concerned about your health, Joseph."

"I'm feeling better. All I need is hard work and a challenge. I want to test myself! Will my ideas succeed here as they did in St. Louis? Will New Yorkers like my kind of newspaper? Look, Kate—" he spread out on the marble-topped table a copy of the New York *Times*. She stood at his shoulder and they examined it together. "Raymond of the *Times* is considered one of the shrewdest and ablest of newspapermen. Financial circles lean on his advice. Conservative political leaders couldn't get along without his information for them. And here are his front-page stories!—'The Funding Bill Passed'; 'Apportionment Problems'; 'Death of Governor Foster in Ohio'; 'The Control of the Senate'; 'Pennsylvania Politics'; 'River and Harbor Bill'; 'Civil Service Reform.' The rest of the paper is the same. It's easy to see the *Times* isn't written for the ordinary man and woman. It's written for specialists, for the insiders, for the people who are in politics or top businesses. And these stories aren't news! They are written as articles."

He walked to the bookcases between the windows and then circled the room slowly, pausing at the fireplace to kick absentmindedly at a log.

"None of the New York papers are written for the general public. Bennett of the *Herald* comes closest to it. He prints stories of human interest. He's witty and amusing and people read him for the scandals he rakes up. But I don't think everything should be treated as a joke. What is it that interests all of us? The drama of our own lives—birth, marriage, accidents, tragedies, the crimes we commit ourselves and those that are practiced on us, the struggle to make life better and easier for us. Death, too. And that drama isn't often a comedy."

Kate listened, thrilled in spite of herself. It seemed to her for the first time he was putting into words his revolutionary ideas.

He went on: "None of the New York newspapers are written for the general public. They think their circulations are big. They are nothing! Nothing, that is, to what they could be if they were written so that everyone—workingman and businessman, housewife and politician—would find something in them of interest. These editors don't know a news story when they see it. The *World* announces that there is going to be a celebration over the opening of the Brooklyn Bridge—*in one paragraph!* That's all! One of the biggest news stories of this year: the opening of that bridge has been talked about on the streets of this city; everyone is wondering when it is going to be; everyone wants to be there—and Hurlbert gives it one paragraph! Kate, I want to try my ideas here. I want a newspaper here!"

"I don't know what to say. Don't decide tonight. Sleep on it, dear. Consider what it will mean: the work and the strain on you."

Kate woke suddenly in the middle of the night. A light was shining under a crack of the parlor door. She heard footsteps on the other side of that door. Hurriedly she slipped on a robe and went out.

"Joseph—?"

He was sitting quietly, the long slender fingers of one hand shading his eyes. When he looked at her the eyes were deeply troubled and unhappy. Never had she seen him look like that.

"I've been sitting here thinking what an absolute fool I am. To believe that I could come into this city and compete with the biggest newspapers in America; to start with the *World* which has hardly any subscriptions; to start without any financial backing except the earnings of the *Post-Dispatch*! I was planning to gamble away all our security, just to satisfy my belief that my kind of newspaper is needed in this town."

Impetuously, Kate flared at him. "It is needed here! And so are you. A presidential election is coming up this year and—"

"And that is what made me really see my folly. Do you know what Dana and Raymond are, what Greeley used to be? Kingmakers. Makers of senators and presidents. Capable of building a political party or tearing one down. They crack their editorial whip and all Washington dances. And I thought I could compete with them!"

His wife was as shocked as she was dismayed. Joseph had always had supreme confidence in his ability.

"You can," she said slowly, "if you want to. Dana and Raymond were once—as Greeley was—able to do all these things you say they did. But times have changed. Remember how you and Thomas Davidson used to tell me that the greatest advance in this country was not the opening of the West after the Civil War, but the opening of people's minds? That people have learned to *read and write*?

125

That they had to, in order to keep up with industry, so they could do their jobs? It won't be Dana or anyone else—not even Joseph Pulitzer—who will be kingmakers any more. It will be the people of this country who decide the elections."

"*If* they get the facts. *If* they get the truth." He leaned forward. Excited color was stealing back into his face. "If they have a newspaper that tells them honestly what is going on. Kate, it isn't *me* I have to trust. It's the people. You are right. We will stay here and make the *World* into that kind of a newspaper. You've convinced me I can do it!"

"I have?" Bewildered, Kate only then realized what she had done. "But I wanted you to have a vacation!" she wailed.

The next day the papers were signed. The first installment of the sale price was paid.

On the evening of May 10, 1883, Pulitzer drove in a hired carriage to Park Row. Here, at No. 31–32 was the building he now owned. As he alighted and paid off the driver, he stood for a moment looking at the modest exterior. Down the street he could see the buildings of two of the nation's great newspapers: the New York *Times,* and the *Tribune.* Against them, and against Bennett of the *Herald* and Dana of the *Sun,* he was to pit his strength. Against them the little *World* was a pygmy among giants.

He walked into the building.

It was quiet and orderly. The staff members were getting out the paper for the next morning and they were taking their time, much more interested in their new publisher and the rumors about him than they were in what they were doing. Heads went up. Doors cautiously opened.

He was met, ceremoniously, in the lobby by William Henry Hurlbert, the editor. It was Hurlbert who set the leisurely and dignified tone of the place; his elegant and polished editorials were the only asset that held their readers and he knew it. Would Mr. Pulitzer care to see his office that morning? Mr. Pulitzer would. But he would see it after he had started at the basement and gone through every floor in the building, every single room, every cubicle, and met every single person in the place.

By the end of the hour Hurlbert was tottering with fatigue. He limped away to his own office and left the new owner alone in his.

Pulitzer sat, letting the *feel* of this particular newspaper world sink into him. It was nothing like the feeling he had had that first day at the *Post-Dispatch*. Then he had been caught in an emotion blended of anger and pity over the neglect of what to him had been a living thing. He had wanted to scrub its dirt off, mend its torn places, clean out its filthy bed, heal it and make it well again. His lightness of heart the night he had made the agreement with Dillon he remembered very well.

Here it was as if everything was dead. Could he revive it? Joseph thought of the rooms below him and the people in them: nicely paneled offices; clean, sunny, airy and well-lighted city desk room; efficient bookkeeping equipment, the latest in files and cabinets; a fine, modern press on the first floor; a staff in clean, good clothes and good manners and competent knowledge of their trade—yet walking around as if on eggshells, whispering. Not talking. *Why?* The flat of his palm smacked the desk in front of him like a pistol shot. They were dead—the whole building was dead—the paper was dead!

He restrained himself long enough to look through yesterday's issue and today's copy. Then he read every other paper: the *Times,* the *Tribune,* the *Herald,* the *Sun,* the *Reporter,* the *Journal.* He read them all and made rapid notes. Soon the yellow pad of paper in front of him was covered with his jottings; he tore that off and started a second and a third and a fourth. Then he was ready. He walked out of the office and to the head of the stair well.

"Hurlbert!" he roared.

In five minutes the calm of the *World* was literally ripped apart. "Send this man in here"—jabbing a finger at a piece of copy—

"and tell the bookkeeper I want to see him. I'm sending a postal message—get me a messenger boy. Tell the reporters I want to see each one of them, one at a time, right away! Today's edition will go out as you have it set up but we are starting right now to plan the next. Who are you? Oh, yes. Nym Crinkle, that's your pen name, isn't it?"

"Yes. It's really Wheeler but—"

"All right, Wheeler. I like this column. It is good. Almost the only thing in the whole paper that is any good. Give me another one like it tomorrow and we'll get along fine. Hurlbert! where's that messenger boy? Oh, let's see—you're the business manager. There aren't enough frames in the composing room. Thirty-three aren't nearly enough for this paper. Order more. Immediately! I want them here tomorrow."

"Tomorrow? I can't—"

"I said *tomorrow*. Hurlbert! Where is that man! Where'd he go? —oh, there you are! Here's a statement for today's paper."

"It will be difficult to insert it at this late hour, Mr. Pulitzer. May I suggest instead that we run it tomorrow?"

The new owner fixed him with a baleful eye. "Pull your editorial. Run this in its place. Hurry up, man. Now, you," he said to another, "you call yourself a reporter and you write a story like this? Where are your facts? Why does the *Herald* have the same story but with all the facts, all the names, all the places—and you have nothing but a confused jumble of words about *somebody* planning a protest petition about the stoves always catching on fire in the horse-drawn trams. *Was* there a fire? *Do* those stoves smoke so much passengers can't abide them? What trams? Where? Who owns them? Who made up this petition protest? What is the name of the company who owns the trams? What do they say about this? Did you interview any passengers to get their impressions?"

"It was such an unimportant story, Mr. Pulitzer," the luckless reporter answered, feebly.

128

"There—is—no—such—thing—as—an—unimportant—story! Do you understand that, all of you? If a story is important enough to be printed in the *World* it is important enough to get all the facts and that you do your best to treat every single story as if it were the Page One lead. This I want to hammer into your heads and if it doesn't penetrate"—as usual when he was worked up, the slight Germanic accent was noticeable and made the words even more impressive—"then you no longer work for me! But you still do work for me and I will give you another chance. Listen. A man is going to die tonight in the prison at White Plains. He is a murderer. I want you to go up there and get a last-minute interview with him. Find out what he is thinking. Is he remorseful? Why did he commit the murder? Is he defiant? What does the warden think of him and the other prisoners? Maybe you can get something from them. Stay with him until the end and get every last little detail."

The reporter swallowed. He had no stomach for this assignment. The protest rose in his throat: it's horrible—they won't let me— then he took another look at Pulitzer's face and hurried out of the room.

"Now, you," he said, indicating two uneasy gentlemen of the press who had been standing by waiting for the acid to be poured out on their heads, "I'll tell you later what's wrong with your work, but right now I want you to cover the big windstorm last night in New Jersey. Standard Oil tanks were hit by lightning. It should have been in today's paper but it isn't too late. This is going to be our lead feature on the front page, so you had better cover it completely. The *Times* and the *Herald* did a poor job on it; that's just fine. I want you to go out on the streets where the damage was the greatest and talk to everyone. Get their personal stories of what it felt like to live through the night with the wind howling around them, shaking their houses and blowing down trees. Go to City Hall and get the estimated damage. Go to the police station. Go to the hospitals and talk to the injured. And then come back and write your stories—and they had better be good!"

The reporters started out the door when he called them back. "I'm not sure that I made myself clear. When you talk to people I want the emotions of those people. I want our readers to know what it is like when a tree falls on the roof of a house and someone is hurt and the family runs out into the night crying and screaming —and they see their child or their father taken away in an ambulance, and then in the morning they go back and find their few pitiful possessions—their dishes, their furniture—broken and smashed." He made dramatic gestures, his voice rising to pathos. Then it changed abruptly. "That's the way I want it. You can go now."

The editor protested. "Our readers aren't accustomed to this sort of—of—sensational writing, Mr. Pulitzer."

Pulitzer didn't even look at him as he barked: "If we had to depend on your few readers, Mr. Hurlbert, we'd be out of business in a week. Mr. Crickmore?—your sporting page is fine. I have absolutely no criticism of it. A good style you have." The sporting editor almost reeled down the stairs in his surprise.

"What else are we planning for the front page?" Hurlbert was subdued. He let his face reflect his distaste for the new methods.

"I'm asking for a volunteer. I want someone"—his eyes swept the three reporters still in the room—"who has both boldness and finesse, because getting this story will require both. I have heard a rumor that James Keane is planning to sell his collection of paintings. They are rare and valuable. Now why would Mr. James Keane be selling his paintings?" He studied each man in turn.

One said: "Keane is a millionaire. I suppose he has his whims."

Another said: "He is supposed to be one of the biggest financiers on Wall Street. If he is selling his paintings perhaps he's getting a little shaky. Maybe his position isn't as secure as is commonly thought."

130

The third man said: "Nonsense. Everyone knows Keane is sound. I'd suggest that his taste may be changing, not his financial status. He may be tired of his pictures, though I've heard he has a Stuart in his collection and he's crazy about it."

Pulitzer pointed at the second man who had spoken. "I'll take you. Your answer shows that you do your own thinking. You have a little of the skepticism that all good newspapermen must have. Just because everyone says Keane is sound doesn't mean he really is. To me there is something very strange about a rich man selling paintings that he greatly treasures. Go interview him."

He handed a cablegram to one of the others. "Rewrite this. It isn't much of a story but a revolt in Haiti is news. One of the first things we will have to do is get a good correspondent out there. This man won't do. He sends a cablegram—and to save a few dollars gives us nothing but a few grains of a story." He motioned them all out. "Now leave me alone. I have work to do."

An hour later the day's edition was handed to him, still wet from the press. He ignored it all except for the statement he had written in place of the editorial. It read in part:

The entire *World* newspaper property has been purchased by the undersigned, and will from this day be under different management—different in men, measures and methods—different in purpose, policy and principle—different in objects and interests—different in sympathy and convictions—different in head and heart. . . .

There is room in this great and glowing city for a journal that is not only cheap but bright, not only bright but large, not only large but truly democratic—dedicated to the cause of the people rather than that of purse potentates—devoted more to the news of the New than the Old World, that will expose all fraud and sham, fight all public evils and abuses—that will serve and battle for the people with earnest sincerity. In the

131

cause for that end, solely, the new *World* is hereby enlisted and committed to the attention of the intelligent public.

Joseph Pulitzer

It wasn't well written. He had dashed it off. But he was satisfied with what it said.

There was a tap on the door. A messenger boy poked his head in.

"Well—at last! Why are you so late?"

"I don't work here. I work for the telegraph company. Mr. Hurlbert asks me to look in once a day for any messages."

"From now on you work for me. Whatever they pay you I'll raise it. Report at ten in the morning; you'll work late but I'll pay you well."

"Gee! It's a deal!" his cocky swagger pleased his new boss.

On his way down the stairs the messenger boy was stopped by Hurlbert. "Let me see that," he ordered. He looked at the message, address and the name on it: John Cockerill, Linden Hotel, St. Louis, Missouri. "Come at once—" Hurlbert did not bother to read any more. The message was the handwriting on the wall for him. He set his old-fashioned hat squarely on his head and took himself and his wounded pride out of the *World* building forever.

On May 11th the Pulitzer-edited issue of the *World* hit the newsstands. Although by his own standards it was nothing to brag about, it caused a wide ripple of excitement in several areas of the city. From their entrenched, solid positions other newspaper publishers read it with a patronizing attitude but also with alarm. Pulitzer, they felt, was a crazy young Lochinvar out of the West, doomed to fail. A flash in the pan. But his style was disturbing. It might just appeal to some people. The storm story, for instance. Headlined "The Deadly Lightning!" subheaded "Six Lives and One Million Dollars Lost," and the two columns packed with human interest stories. And the article on Keane—if Keane really was on the rocks then the *World* might win for itself a reputation for shrewd-

132

ness. They turned from the account of the murderer's last night with genteel disgust; he had refused a priest, said the *World,* and shouted, "I'm not a Catholic. I'm a Democrat!" and went to his death protesting: "Yer hangin' an innocent man!"

The old readers of the paper were stunned. What had happened to the conservative policy and to Hurlbert's conservative editorials?

There was still another group who took a sharp interest. The news dealers had quick eyes for boosting sales. They noticed that people who came up to their stands to buy a paper, even though they might be regular purchasers of the *Times* or the *Tribune* or the *Herald* or some other sheet, stopped to glance at the front page of the *World,* took another look—and bought it. The news dealers, cannily, moved the *World* up to the front of the counters. Maybe it would catch the eye of the casual passer-by and make him *want* to buy a paper.

"How come? How come, Joe, you're pushing the *World?*" a hackney cab driver, waiting for a fare, asked a dealer.

"No, sir! I never push one paper over another. I'm neutral, I am. But," he added, lowering his voice, "I read it and I liked it. It's different. It jumps the news right out at you. See that bakery shop there? Anderson owns it. Always buys the *Herald.* Today he takes a look at this story of the storm in the *World* and he says to me 'Why, that's Flossie Mayhew, my aunt! In New Jersey. They've got her own words about how she yelled for help when her chimney caught on fire in that terrible wind.' Anderson bought six copies to show all his family. And that murder story—brrrr!—fair gives you the shudders, it does. I can't get it out of my mind; I'm not sure they should print such things but it's Heaven's warning to all of us, it is."

The cab driver bought a paper.

The furious tempo that Pulitzer had set that first day at the *World* did not slacken. If anything, with the coming of John Cockerill and McGuffin from St. Louis, the pace increased. Both of the imported men were as stormy and determined as their boss. Every day there was an editorial council and their furious arguing could be heard all over the floor. Peter Townsend, one of Hurlbert's staff who was kept on the Pulitzer pay roll, wrote to a friend of his:

> I hardly knew the office. A cyclone had struck . . . men were hurrying around. . . . JP seemed to be everywhere . . . now arguing with a reporter, now dashing to the composing room, now suddenly descending on the market editor. . . . He loves argument. . . . He told me once that it is in debate that a man's qualities appear—above all, whether he has moral courage. . . .

If it was debate and argument and courage he wanted, he got it from Cockerill and McGuffin.

John Cockerill had been somewhat sobered from the St. Louis tragedy, but he was still a robust and hearty fighter. Not a tall man, he gave the impression of bigness. The heavy mustache on his upper lip, curled and twisted on the ends, seemed to be constantly bristling with indignation and energy. The rest of his face was smoothly shaven. His hair, parted in the middle and dipping slightly over his forehead, was always combed just so. He wasted no time in Pulitzer's nervous gestures of running his fingers through beard and hair when disturbed. Cockerill's square-set body held a controlled, disciplined dynamo inside it.

At the first council meeting he outlined new ideas.

"I've been doing a lot of thinking—"

"Heaven help us," Pulitzer commented dryly.

Cockerill ignored this. "I've been thinking what we can do to improve the looks of the paper. I want to experiment with bold, black type for the leads to catch the eye. As it is now, all the stories run right into each other. Then," he went on, with an embattled eye on McGuffin, "I'm going to separate each news item with white space. And at least a quarter of an inch between lead and sublead and sublead and the copy itself."

As he expected, McGuffin rose to the bait with a roar of injury. "You want to ruin us financially before we even get started? New type! White spaces! Empty white spaces when we need every inch we can get for what we need to print? Would you like it if maybe we printed a whole page blank? Or we pulled out the ads so you could have room for your white space?"

The argument raged. Cockerill won by the trick of turning McGuffin's wrath against Pulitzer. "You think I'm the one who is going to cost us too much money? Wait until you get the bill for all the pictures Joe is planning for the Brooklyn Bridge spread!"

"Pictures!" McGuffin tore at his shirt collar.

"Yes, pictures. Drawings. Cuts," Pulitzer explained, his voice rising as he tried to drown out the manager's explosive protests. "We've got a newspaper here that is practically unknown to the public in general. I have to have bait. I'm going to have a drawing on the front page of every issue, so that when the *World* is folded on the newsstands it will impel people to notice it."

Shaky as their finances were, he got his pictures, and Cockerill his type and his new, widely spaced make-up. The *World* was gambling and it was no time to pinch pennies.

McGuffin's concern about spending unnecessary money—much as his employer valued this trait in him—almost brought the paper to disaster in the first week. He cut off the ice for the drinking water in the composing room and refused to give the men soap with which to wash their hands.

The men were furious. They had long wanted to make the *World* a union shop and McGuffin's action was the spark that set off revolt. They walked out. They went on strike, demanding ice in their drinking water, soap in their washroom—and the right to join a trade union, with the higher wages that would bring them.

John R. O'Donnell, president of the Typographical Union's local No. 6, presented the strike demands. Pulitzer invited him and

135

Cockerill to Keenan's Café next door to the *World* Building to talk things over.

Cockerill was for fighting the demands. Pulitzer disagreed.

"We can't have a strike. We've worked for days on that Brooklyn Bridge spread for tomorrow. We're counting on it to make a splash in this town that will bring the *World* to everyone's attention. Tell the men they have their demands, O'Donnell."

McGuffin was slow in carrying out the order. The men had gone back to work when Pulitzer wandered into the composing room several hours later. It was hot in there. He stooped to get a drink from the water bucket and immediately spat it out in disgust. It was lukewarm.

"McGuffin!" he roared. "Get that ice!" He was as personally outraged as the composing room men themselves.

The Brooklyn Bridge double-page spread, across two full inside pages, crowded with pictures and drawings, was a tremendous success. It had been preceded several days before by the kind of journalism that was typically Pulitzer's—the crusade on behalf of the people's interests. In this case it was a call, repeated day after day, to eliminate the five-cent toll for pedestrians crossing the bridge.

Even earlier the *World* had startled its readers with a plain-spoken editorial entitled "Our Aristocracy." It was bitter sarcasm directed against the rich and fashionable who thought their furs and their jewels and their bad manners made them aristocrats, and it ended with a tribute to the laboring men who built the country, calling them the only real American aristocracy.

And on May 17th the *World* published its platform:

1. Tax luxuries
2. Tax inheritances
3. Tax large incomes
4. Tax monopolies

5. Tax the privileged corporation
6. A tariff for revenue
7. Reform the civil service
8. Punish corrupt officers
9. Punish vote buying
10. Punish employers who coerce their employees in elections.

These were all burning issues. With these two editorials and with the dazzling double-page spread of the Brooklyn Bridge, the circulation of the *World* took a decisive, unprecedented turn upward. Newsstands could not keep up with the demand. Rival editors, still muttering 'flash in the pan,' were bewildered. Nothing like this skyrocket leap into popularity had been seen before.

The answer was simple. People were hungry for news, for facts, written in an easy, colorful style they could readily understand. They liked a paper that stated boldly it was for their interests against the rich and powerful, and they liked it still better when it lived up to its statement.

Now that the first hurdle had been overcome and the staff was enlarged, Pulitzer was free to do what he most wanted: to launch into the presidential election campaign.

He had his eye on one man. The governor of New York was Grover Cleveland. In an editorial which called for all the forces of the Democratic party to heal their splits and work together, Pulitzer inserted the thought-provoking tag that they should find someone like Grover Cleveland. This was the first suggestion of Cleveland as a possible candidate.

The *World* was in on the ground floor. It had picked the man who was to win. The *World's* campaign for Cleveland established it as a political power to be reckoned with. The Democratic machine swung into line; the voters liked the New York governor's

137

record; the *World* kept up a steady stream of pro-Cleveland editorials.

He was elected. Many years later Cleveland was to say:

. . . the contest was so close it may be said without reservation that if it had lacked the forceful and potent advocacy of Democratic principles at that time by the New York *World* the result might have been reversed.

It was not to be supposed that the other New York papers sat idly by and watched this newcomer take away their readership. If it was this undignified, sensational kind of news people wanted, the *Sun* and the *Tribune* and the *Times* would give it to them. But old habits were strong. They imitated the *World,* but reluctantly. Day after day big news stories were ignored by them and splashed across the pages of Pulitzer's newspaper.

In their alarm, both Bennett of the *Herald* and Dana of the *Sun* took strong actions—which boomeranged so badly that they alone were hurt and the *World* got the benefit of their mistakes.

The *World* was selling for two cents a copy at that time. Bennett cut the price of the *Herald* from three to two cents to fight Pulitzer. But rather than lose the profit he had been making at the higher price, he cut down the percentage the news dealers were getting from him, from one half to one third of a cent a copy. The dealers retaliated. They wouldn't handle the *Herald.* Bennett was forced to build his own newsstands and hire his own dealers. He lost heavily in sales and the *World* picked up his old readers.

Then Dana backed the wrong man for president. Partly because of a petty grudge against Cleveland and partly to show the upstart *World* that he was still the newspaper editor whose political wisdom was unquestioned, he came out for Benjamin Butler. During the last days of the campaign the circulation of the *Sun* dropped from 137,000 to 85,000 a day. Again the *World* benefited.

In the first three months of Pulitzer's taking over the *World* circulation rose from 22,761 to 39,000 a day. By the end of the year the circulation was on a par with the biggest in the city and by another year it had passed all the others!

The *World* had arrived. It was on top. A new kind of journalism had come into being.

By that time his staff had come to view their publisher with the awe of someone half devil, half god. They were terrified at his wrath when they made a serious mistake; their admiration for his wisdom was almost reverence. No longer did he write copy himself or edit it or write heads or make up the paper—though he could still do all these things in a pinch. His true genius came out now in his ability to pick the right man for the right job, to instill in others his own fervor and excitement for work and to keep men balanced against each other so that out of turbulence came a fresh and lively newspaper every day.

He still worked hard. He still drove himself. Cockerill and Kate Pulitzer entered into a conspiracy to try to make him relax and take things easier.

But how could he explain to them, even to a beloved wife and a close friend, the terror that had been sitting on his shoulder from the first day he walked into the *World* Building? If he failed—! And the smallest thing, a little detail missed, a false story, could trip him. That first week before Cockerill had come he had had to be responsible for everything; he had even moved his office temporarily to a tiny cubbyhole off the composing room to be closer to the workers. He used to leave Kate at the Fifth Avenue Hotel early in the morning and come back to her so late at night the sky was already getting pink at the approach of dawn.

Alone in the building at night, reading copy and planning the pages for the next day, Joseph Pulitzer could be seized with a doubt and fear that tore at his already overworked nerves. He had never given his body the rest it needed. Now he piled a load on himself that was more than muscle and nerves could take. Several times those first weeks he found himself growing dizzy and faint as he walked down the stairs. Behind his weakened eyes was a constant throb of pain.

The fact that the *World* was now an established success only piled more responsibility on his shoulders. He had now three editions to cope with: a *Morning World,* an *Evening World* and a *Sunday World.* Editors and staff had to be found for all three. Crises developed daily on every one of them.

In addition, during the Cleveland presidential campaign, he had allowed himself to be elected representative from the Ninth District. He was sent to Washington to take his seat in the Forty-ninth Congress.

Kate protested.

"It was bad enough to have you working day and night at the *World.* At least I could visit you there and Ralph could play around in your office and realize he did have a father. And you were home for breakfast. But now!" It was wintertime. The two of them were crossing Gramercy Park to the home they had leased facing it. The snow was falling and the cold had even whipped some color into her too-pale cheeks. Joseph looked at her and his conscience hurt him. Little Katherine had died a month before. The tragedy had been terribly, grievously hard on both of them but more so on Kate because he had less time to think of it. He had no right to be away from her at this time.

"I was an imbecile to have run for office. I am criticized in Washington for not being in Congress often enough; Cockerill complains I neglect the *World.* I proclaim that the paper is free of any political ties, then I become a Democratic representative, tied to a party machine, forced to line up in House debates with my Democratic colleagues whether I agree with them or not. I was a fool. But more than that: how could I treat so lightly the privilege of being the husband of the most beautiful woman in New York

140

and the father of the best children that I hardly ever see them? I will resign tomorrow."

She squeezed his arm gratefully and took one of his gloved hands in hers, inside her muff. "I was beginning to think you were deserting me for another woman."

"Well, to tell you the truth, I was. I am."

"Joseph!"

Never demonstrative in public, this time he broke his rule. He caught her close to him while she struggled to get away. "Not only that, Kate—a French woman. Half French, half American. Even more beautiful than you are, dear."

"Who *is* she!"

"The 'Statue of Liberty,' Kate."

It was true. Joseph had become obsessed with the stone goddess. While he was a congressman he had stumbled across a shameful secret that was kept from the public. The people of France had raised a million francs and commissioned the great sculptor Auguste Bartholdi to create a great statue of Liberty as their gift of friendship to America. The statue was finished. It lay, crated, gathering dust in a French warehouse, because Congress had refused year after year to raise enough money for the gigantic pedestal to hold the goddess high enough on Bedloe's Island so that her torch might be seen by every ship entering New York Harbor.

Joseph was determined to rescue her from this shameful betrayal. He issued an appeal through the pages of the *World*:

Money must be raised to complete the pedestal for the Bartholdi statue. It would be an irrevocable disgrace to New York City and the American Republic to have France send us this splendid gift without our having provided even so much as a landing place for it. . . .

The *World* is the people's paper, and it now appeals to the people to come forward and raise this money. The $250,000 that the making of the statue cost was paid in by the masses of the French people—by the workingmen, the tradesmen, the shopgirls, the artisans—by all, irrespective of class or condition. Let us respond in like manner. It is not a gift from the millionaires of France to the millionaires of America but a gift of the whole people of France to the whole people of America. . . .

The appeal ran next to a full story of how the statue had been conceived, and how built. There was a drawing of the goddess.

The response was electric, unheard of. Money poured into the *World* offices. It came mostly from the poor—a dollar from a family taken from meager savings, a nickel from an office boy, a collection from an evening where artists contributed their services, thirty-five cents from an old woman, five dollars from the wages of shopgirls, contributions from clubs and trade unions, a jar of pennies that a storekeeper brought in as the gift from himself and his customers. Letters came with the money. Printed in the *World*, they made a strong bond between newspaper and readers because they were doing something together for a common purpose.

It took time. A lot of pennies and nickels and dollars were needed, but—finally—on August 11, 1886, the story broke in headlines in the *World* that one hundred thousand dollars had been collected. The goal was reached.

Now, as the statue was loaded onto the French ship *Isère* for its voyage to its new home, other newspapers and the great statesmen in Washington belatedly came to support the project and to claim some credit. The public laughed. The "Statue of Liberty" was coming because *they* had made it possible—they and Pulitzer of the *World*.

His own emotions, as he stood with other dignitaries of the city and the nation at the official dedication on October 28th, were a mixture of fierce pride and deep humility. There it stood! The beautiful goddess with the torch of liberty and the inscription on it a passionate promise of justice and freedom:

> Give me your tired, your poor,
> Your huddled masses yearning to breathe free,
> The wretched refuse of your teeming shore,
> Send these, the homeless, tempest-tossed, to me:
> I lift my lamp beside the golden door.

The statue was built and designed by Frenchmen; its inscription written by a Jewish poetess Emma Lazarus; its pedestal promoted by an Austrian-born, Jewish-Catholic newspaper publisher; the money for it subscribed by Americans of all possible origins and races and religions. The dedication was one of those rare moments when it seemed as if a whole nation bowed its head to an idea.

When he had first become a newspaper publisher in St. Louis, Pulitzer had ordered a strict ban on dialect stories or jokes that reflected on anyone's creed, race or nationality.

Among the crusades of the *World* there were many against forms of discrimination. It strongly attacked the Ku Klux Klan for its white-robed, night-riding violence and spoke of the courage of the Negro people for withstanding this faceless, treacherous cruelty. When, in later years, Theodore Roosevelt invited the great Negro leader Booker T. Washington to the White House, the *World* was one of the few newspapers that applauded the action in an editorial.

Other editors were not as scrupulous about chauvinistic name-calling as he. Not only was Pulitzer caricatured, with his head ten times the size of his body and his nose five times the size of his head, but the language attributed to him was what, in the minds of these editors, passed crudely for German-Jewish dialect. The fact that he was Jewish was used again and again as an insult, in print.

Pulitzer's orders to his editors were: Ignore it. No retaliation in kind.

Except for that one restriction, everything else went in a fight. He would swap blow for blow, verbally and in print, with any opponent. Cartoons and caricatures were a favorite weapon of his. The outspoken language of both the *World* and the *Post-Dispatch* became famous; evildoers squirmed to see their names mentioned and dreaded to read the story about themselves.

eight

When Joseph Pulitzer first bought the *World* its issues ran to only eight pages and six columns to a page. The paper was soon expanded to ten pages, the columns increasing to seven. A *Sunday World* was created and in its second year its readership was 150, 054 every week. New presses had to be bought to handle the three issues: *Morning, Evening* and *Sunday Worlds*. Annexes were found, with one building as far out as Brooklyn.

The editorial management was becoming too much for Pulitzer and Cockerill to handle. Ballard Smith was enticed away from the *Herald* to be managing editor. Cockerill was promoted to "editor in charge."

Headlines—big ones—were one of Smith's innovations. He was also responsible for bringing to importance the personal interview with people of prominence. Because of his own social connections he broke through the icy barrier of the "four hundred" and made its doings common gossip for the pages of the *World*.

Two such strong men as Smith and Cockerill were bound to clash. Pulitzer was caught in the middle of their arguments but he let them go on. It became a principle with him to keep authority divided at the top. As the years went on this policy resulted sometimes in the wildest kind of confusion with no one sure of authority, but it also meant that no one individual's ideas—not even his own—

could become dictatorial or so hardened they couldn't change. He felt that men worked best collectively.

In 1887 Pulitzer began another election campaign that was to prove disastrous to him, personally.

He had had his eye on a young man, De Lancy Nicoll, as a likely prospect for district attorney. As an assistant in that office, Nicoll had been instrumental in helping the *World* to ferret out the fraud behind a streetcar franchise, and in a great public scandal he had succeeded in indicting the crook Jacob Sharp and in putting the bribed aldermen into jail. Sharp had killed himself rather than face justice.

At first Charles Dana of the *Sun* went along with the Nicoll candidacy for district attorney. It seemed it would be an easy and natural victory. Everyone realized that Nicoll and the *World* had worked closely together on the streetcar scandal, but the young man was of such unimpeachable reputation it did not seem to Pulitzer that anyone could resent his having a kind of sponsorship of the candidate.

He was mistaken. Suddenly Dana turned, in an unbelievably slashing, personal attack, against both him and Nicoll. Every day Dana's pen, dipped in acid, spattered across front page and editorial page of the *Sun* his opinions of the *World*:

> The *World* has taken up the cause of Mr. Nicoll after the fashion of a highwayman with a pistol. . . . The *World* breaks into the affairs of the city as train robbers enter an express car . . . this would-be Sahib of the Bohemian race [meaning Pulitzer] . . . this renegade Jew . . . the Democrats of New York will not yield one hair's breadth to the insolent demands of that political road agent. . . . The candidate who stands for boss dictation is Nicoll and the boss behind Nicoll is Judas Pulitzer, who exudes the venom of a snake and wields the bludgeon of a bully. . . .

The *World* editors and publishers were stunned by Dana's sudden about-face—although a look at their own rising subscriptions and the *Sun*'s falling ones might have indicated the reason. But when Dana also raked up the old story of Cockerill's killing a man in St. Louis in a duel and implied that Pulitzer had freed Cockerill by bribing the court, this was too much. The *World* let loose an editorial blast of its own:

> These statements are malicious lies, about what might be expected from Charles Ananias Dana. . . . The revival of the St. Louis affair . . . is worthy of a . . . mortgaged, broken-down calumniator in the last agonies of humiliation. . . . Two grand juries thoroughly investigated the case of Mr. Cockerill and refused even to return a bill. . . . No influence, direct or otherwise, was ever employed upon the public prosecutor. This is a plain statement of fact which mortgaged Dana, with all his ingenuity as an unmitigated scoundrel and actuated by a hatred which amounts to insanity, cannot controvert.

The election campaign mounted to a fury of activity in both the Nicoll camp and that of his opponent Fellows. Pulitzer worked night and day, speaking, writing, planning; he was away from his desk only to confer with the Nicoll campaign managers or to speak in his behalf at some luncheon or meeting. Kate was frantic. She begged him to rest and resorted to scheming with Cockerill to see that Joseph had a rare evening to spend at home. Even then she saw that he was like a man consumed with fever; his cheeks had burning red spots, his eyes were bloodshot; he jumped at every crackle of a log burning in the fireplace.

It was a long and dirty fight. Actually there were two battles going on: the Nicoll-Fellows contest and the separate attack to try to kill the *World*. Dana confused the two.

Fellows won. His opponent was a young and relatively unknown man and Fellows was backed by all the weight of the Democratic party machine. Charles Dana had one exultant, gloating moment of belief in his personal triumph. For him this meant that the *Sun* was again the power it had once been, the power behind political thrones. His editorial that day came from a man who believed he had crushed his enemy:

> And now, Pulitzer, a word with you!
> You stand before this community in the same startling light that you stood in some years ago in St. Louis when your career of scandal and blackmail culminated in murder. . . . We could wish with all our hearts, Pulitzer, that St. Louis had possessed a stronger stomach. You might have stayed there. . . . We wish, Pulitzer, that you had never come.
> But that you are here is indisputable, and that the public has found you out is obvious. In this experimental stage of universal sentiment it is not possible to state definitely what your fate will be. We do not know. We can only see clearly that it will be something unpleasant. . . .
> Move on, Pulitzer, move on!

Dana thought he had smashed the *World* but all he had done was to help win an election. Pulitzer answered the gloating with the cold, hard facts which his competitor would have liked to forget:

> The editor of the *World* accepts the hatred of Mr. Dana as a compliment. . . . He especially appreciates the agonized heart-cry of Mr. Dana, which appears in yesterday's issue of the *Sun*, in the midst of a literary muck-heap, which could only be found on the editorial page of that paper:
> "We wish, Pulitzer, that you had never come."
> Nothing could be truer than this. From his innermost soul the broken and humiliated editor of the *Sun* wishes that the regeneration of the *World* had never taken place. In four

148

years' time he has seen the circulation of his paper dwindle until it has fallen into the third rank; he has seen his dividends vanish; his income swept away. . . .

Sad, no doubt, Mr. Dana is, that somebody came who could provide the New York public with the newspaper which it wanted. But the man is here, and he will remain. The *World* is stronger and better today than it ever was. . . .

The man is here, and he will remain. Strange that an election of a district attorney, so inconsequential to history, should play such a tragic drama in the lives of both these men: Dana and Pulitzer. For the editor of the *Sun* it was the last, fleeting moment of old glories revived; it was the swan song of both Dana and his paper. Never was he to regain his power and popularity though the *Sun* was to linger on for years.

The man is here, and he will remain. Pulitzer saw, rightly, that losing the election meant no loss to the supremacy of the *World*. But it had been a bitter, terrible, drawn-out fight and his personal involvement in it had been more costly than anything he could have imagined. His own personal tragedy was drawing near.

Late that same month he came as usual to his office. He sat at his desk and pulled toward him a galley proof of copy. Cockerill, on his way into his chief's office with a report, saw him sitting motionless and hunched; for once that straight, proud back was stooped. There was a sound from him, a murmur of astonishment and fearful knowledge. He raised his head and his old friend and co-worker was never to forget the awful look on his face.

"I cannot read a single line! *I cannot see!*"

Late that night Cockerill went to the Pulitzer home. He was met by Kate and by Thomas Davidson who had come east on a visit.

"The doctor says his eyesight will return," she told him. "But he also says that Joseph has punished his body in a way that no

149

human being can stand and he says it is imperative that he rest and have a change of scene, away from newspapers."

"I hope he recovers quickly," said Cockerill. "We need him. With a morning and evening edition—and a Sunday—to get out, it's like having a bear by the tail and you can't let go. I don't relish the responsibility; even with Carvalho and Greaves handling the evening paper it is still—" he broke off, wondering at the gravity and the silence of the other two.

Davidson spoke. "Dinna ye ken what that mon has been through? He came here a young laddie with not a word of the language in him; when he most needed friends he was abused by the soldiers of the Army; after that he starved—aye, he starved and was cold and had to beat his way to St. Louis; it was no easy for him. When I first met him he was a hungry boy—hungry for food as well as for the books—many a time I think my cup of tea was all he had for the day. He read and he studied; he would forego the meal for the book. He strained his eyes. And when he became a reporter for the *Westliche Post* and ever since that time he has worked like a slave! People look at him and they say he is a rich mon, a canny one, a lucky one—but do they know the insults, the humiliation, the savage and ruffian persecution Joseph has had to face?"

"I don't want him to come back to work for a long, long time, John," Kate added, quietly. "I am afraid for him."

The trip to California was not a success. The strong sunlight hurt his eyes. He had recovered some of his sight and it seemed to be getting stronger all the time, but the glare was too much for him. A new development alarmed him even more: any sharp noise was an agonizing jolt to his nerves. He could feel it like a blow.

They returned by way of St. Louis. Pulitzer made a brief visit to the *Post-Dispatch*. The paper was doing well and prospering, even though he had given it very little attention. He hated the city and was anxious to leave it. For him his first, beloved paper was

150

spoiled by the memory of the mob swarming around it. He was never to see it or the city again.

Back in New York he forced himself to visit the *World* only rarely, and each brief visit taught him the folly of it. The loud noises of the press, the voices, the scratch of pen on paper—all the familiar sounds that had meant so much to him—now were intolerable. He stayed in New York only long enough to purchase the site for the new building to house the *World*. It was more than coincidence that the spot he picked was the old French's Hotel, at the corner of Park Row and Frankfort Street. This was the very place a bootblack had ordered him to leave years ago because his overcoat was too shabby for the customers.

He left Kate with the children and took ship to Europe to consult with the best doctors he could find. In London, first, then in Paris, he was examined by specialists. Everywhere the verdict was the same: complete absence from any city or any place or person or scene that would even faintly remind him of a newspaper! Where could he find such a place?

An idea had long been forming in his mind; not so much an idea as a dream. Quiet, still waters and the sensation of floating on endless waves, nothing to see but the monotony of the sea about him: a shipboard cruise might be the very cure he was looking for. He always felt better on the brief journeys across the ocean to the Continent. Perhaps a long sea voyage, with no time limit, would be what he needed. There he could guard against any new impact to his failing eyesight or his racked nerves.

Kate joined him, and they began a leisurely slow trip toward India and China and Japan.

He tried to keep his mind off the *World*. It was hard to do. There were questions Cockerill or Carvalho or Smith had to ask him and cables could still reach even to shipboard. He hired Claude Ponsonby, a secretary to read to him and keep him informed and send his instructions about matters dealing with the

151

World or the great building rising on the torn-down foundations of French's Hotel.

En route to India the ship turned into a Grecian port. A cablegram was waiting for him there from Colonel William Davis, his brother-in-law whom he had appointed as a sort of watchdog in the *World* offices to referee the differences between his editors. The message, long and indignant, was really of little importance and had to do with a petty squabble elevated to a major quarrel and demanding an answer from Pulitzer.

It threw him into a passion of rage.

"Intelligent men!" he stormed to Ponsonby, striding up and down the deck of the ship. "Quarreling like children over every least little thing and coming running to me to take sides. When the policy of the *World* is so clear, why cannot they use their own brains to settle these matters? I have told them to consult me on important matters only and this is what they send me!" he crumpled up the message and stepped to the railing to hurl it into the sea. Suddenly he stopped. He clutched the rail.

"How suddenly it has gotten dark." His voice was hushed.

"It's not dark," Ponsonby replied. The sun was glaring down on the blue waters.

"Well, it's dark to me."

The secretary could say nothing. He had the shock of feeling he could not possibly have heard those words.

For a long moment Pulitzer stood silent, frozen, lost in a swinging, whirling void where there was neither light nor time nor space. *Blind!* A moment ago he had been a part of this ship and this port. Even though dimly, he had looked at his fellow passengers and known when they were looking at him; he had seen with his weak eyes the blue water and the fishermen singing in their tiny boats below and the bustle of cargo unloading on the dock and the dazzling white houses with their red-topped roofs of the little town that circled the bay. And now it was all gone. He was alone in the empty, terrifying loneliness that only the blind can know.

"Mr. Pulitzer—"

"Send for Dr. McLane." This was the doctor who had accompanied their party, both as friend and physician. "No, wait—take me below to my cabin. I don't want people staring at me." Beneath the iron control of his voice there was raw anguish.

Ponsonby guided his steps. Once Joseph Pulitzer reached out his hands to feel in front of him, then he quickly dropped them at his sides. That was the typical gesture of a blind man. He would not copy it.

Dr. McLane's verdict after examination was final and nearly hopeless. The retina of one eye had become permanently detached. It would never function again. In the other it was just possible that he might regain—not sight—but enough vision to distinguish light from dark and a solid object if it was right in front of him.

"What can we do, Doctor?" Kate asked. She held Joseph's hand tightly.

"For the eyes? Nothing. The danger comes from the nerves and from the paroxysms that come over your husband with any noise or excitement. You will have to adjust your life so that you can control this, Mr. Pulitzer. You will have to separate yourself from any kind of active life."

"Exile—" Joseph murmured.

"Yes. But first I would suggest you return to New York to see Dr. S. Weir Mitchell. He has had excellent success in treating nervous disorders. I am not too hopeful but I believe we should see him as soon as possible."

They transferred to another ship immediately and started home. At Naples the ship's schedule called for several days of stay, in order to load and unload cargo. McLane took his patient to a darkened room in a Naples hotel so that he could have relief from the noise of the docks. No sooner were they settled in the hotel when gun blasts rattled the very walls of the room! They found that artillery practice had been ordered in the city's fortifications and were scheduled to keep up, hour after hour, for an entire week.

McLane wired to officials in Rome. While they waited an answer the guns went on roaring, all day, all night.

"How does he stand it?" Ponsonby asked the doctor. Tears ran down his cheeks. "Every blast is like a convulsion on his body. He is being crucified! Yet he sits there and listens to me read Goethe to him and talks about Goethe as if nothing was happening to him."

"He is a strong man. Unfortunately his body was never as strong as his will," Kate replied.

The message came back from Rome. For Mr. Joseph Pulitzer, the world-renowned publisher of two mighty American newspapers, for the privilege of having such a great visitor to Naples, the artillery practice would cease. It was a pleasure to do such a small favor for such a man.

They reached New York in October of 1890. Joseph was forty-three years old. He was in the prime of life; but Dr. Weir Mitchell's advice to him, after the examination, was the same as McLane's and it virtually meant that life as he had known it was ended.

The examination took place in the Pulitzers' new home on East 55th Street. After it was over he said good-by to the doctor and rejoined his family in the library. This room of all others he loved the most. Before going abroad he had stocked its shelves with thousands of his favorite books. On one wall were priceless tapestries. He would never see them again.

Kate and the children—Ralph now eleven, Lucille ten, Joseph five, Edith four and the baby Constance only two and sitting in her mother's lap—waited for him. For two hours, until the children's bedtime, the family was together and they talked of ordinary things and listened to Lucille's problems at school and Ralph's

154

excitement over being allowed to "help out" at the *World* building and to the laughter and playing of the younger ones. At last Kate and Joseph were alone.

"What will this mean to us, Joseph?"

He had thought about it and faced the truth. "It will mean long separations from you, Kate. The children need you and you will have to stay here with them. They must go to school; they cannot wander around the face of the earth with me, even if I could stand to be with them that long." One of the bitterest things he had to face was that the normal behavior of his children—their playing, their childish shouts and squabbles and even their laughter—was too noisy for him to bear. "I have given this some thought, Kate. It seems to me that I must reconcile myself to the facts, no matter how unpleasant they are. I am almost blind. I have a wrecked nervous system. I must stop trying to live in a makeshift way. The solution can only be that I make a life for myself that will fit my condition and adapt rooms and places and situations *to me,* instead of trying to adjust to them. We will have to start with soundproofing certain rooms in this house, Kate."

She shuddered. It sounded as if he were talking of his own prison. "That can be done, Joseph."

"But while it is being done I will have to get out of the noise of the city. I plan to buy a yacht, dear. In that way I can go where I please and seek for the quiet I need."

"And I can be with you sometimes!" she knelt by his side.

His hand, groping, touched her face. "I have made you cry, Kate. Forgive me."

"Joseph—!" Even through the film of her tears the verdict seemed unreal. He was big and strong. The tall body, six foot two, was not stooped and the physique seemed to be that of a vigorous, healthy man. His illness had not ravaged his face. There were lines of character and intelligence and suffering in it but the over-all im-

155

pression was one of nobility. Only the dark, thick glasses over his eyes indicated the weakness.

On October 16, 1890, an announcement was made on the front page of the *World* which began:

> Yielding to the advice of his physicians Mr. Joseph Pulitzer has withdrawn entirely from the editorship of the *World*. . . .

A short time later he went on board the yacht *Romola*, to begin the strangest part of his life.

nine

The year before, the cornerstone of the Pulitzer Building had
been laid. Four-year-old Joseph Pulitzer, coached by his smiling
mother, had had the honor of wielding the trowel to mortar the
stone in place. Within it was placed sample copies of newspapers
of the day, a medallion commemorating the fact that the *World*
had reached a circulation of two hundred and fifty thousand a
day, pictures of the Pulitzer family, and other historic mementos.

Now the building was sufficiently completed to permit the
World to be published from there. An immense gold dome sur-
mounted the building and could be seen from the windows of other
newspaper editors. That dome hardly looked to them like a flash in
the pan now!

In turning over the editorial affairs, Pulitzer thought he had hit
upon a perfect scheme. Authority was divided between Colonel
William Davis, his brother-in-law, and Cockerill and George
Turner, the *World*'s business manager. But it didn't work out.
Turner and Cockerill were mortal enemies, jockeying constantly
for power.

To keep the peace, Pulitzer ordered Cockerill to exchange places
with John Dillon of the *Dispatch*. Dillon agreed and came to New
York, but Cockerill did not want to leave the city. So when a
chance came along for him to acquire a small paper of his own,
he quit—but not in anger. "John" and "Joe" were to remain lifelong

friends; never again was the *World* to have an editor who fitted so ably and so well the task of steering the paper along the policies laid down by Pulitzer in his first statement of ownership.

Ballard Smith became editor in chief.

Barely had the new order of things had a chance to get shaken down into routine when a major news story broke. The Homestead steel workers went on strike. Should the *World* favor the company or the strikers? The argument raged back and forth between the editors. The other newspapers, almost unanimously were against the strike, and called the striking workmen *Anarchist!* and *Foreigners! Radicals!*

What was the *World* to do? They had orders not to disturb Pulitzer, but this was too big for them to handle alone. A cable was sent to him on board ship.

His answer asked just one question: What are the facts?

Special reporters were immediately sent to the scene of the strike. It was found that Homestead had hired hundreds of Pinkerton detectives, armed them with guns and set them on the unarmed workers. The climax was a bloody massacre; Pinkerton men drifted down the Allegheny River in gunboats until they came opposite the unarmed mass of workers on shore, fired on them, killing six and injuring scores.

When Pulitzer heard these facts he cabled back: Print that story. Drawings and eyewitness accounts filled the pages of the *World*. Again the paper was to stand alone for what it believed to be right.

And so, in spite of his firm decision to "withdraw entirely from the editorship of the *World*" Pulitzer remained. There were continents and oceans between him and his newspapers for most of his life. Rarely did he come to Chatswold, his home in Bar Harbor, where he could hold conferences with his staff across a table. Yet on almost all important matters of the *World* he, and he alone, made the final decisions, guided policy, hired and fired men—often without ever having met them.

He had been a great reporter, then a great editor. Now, blind, sick, exiled, he was to prove himself still a great publisher and handler of men.

The men who worked at one time or another on the *World* would fill a roster of the greats of journalism: men such as Irvin S. Cobb, Lester A. Walton, who later became ambassador to Liberia, Walter Lippmann, Albert Payson Terhune, better known for his dog stories, Deems Taylor, Heywood Broun, Laurence Stallings and Maxwell Anderson (their great play *What Price Glory* was born in the restaurant on the fourteenth floor of the Pulitzer Building), Winfield R. Sheehan, Franklin P. Adams, Herbert Bayard Swope, Don Seitz and countless others.

William H. Merrill, brilliant editorial writer, was hired away from the Boston *Herald*. Over a period of many years Merrill was to rise to a position of top authority, next to Pulitzer himself. This man was a strange figure in the *World* offices. He was quiet, sedate, forceful only in the keenness of his mind and his ability to handle men and situations. There was no storm or bluster here; all was order and calm. Once, when Congress was preparing to act upon a certain bill, Merrill was expected to write his editorial on it late that night. At his regular hour of six, he picked up hat, coat, gloves and cane to go home.

Someone asked him why he didn't stick around, have his dinner at Keenan's? The news of the bill might be coming in at any moment.

"Because," replied Merrill, "in twenty-five years I have never missed dinner at seven." He continued: "I rise at seven o'clock, breakfast at seven-thirty, read the papers until eight-thirty, ride my horse in Central Park until nine, then take the El downtown. By ten I am at my desk. I lunch at one, finish my work and go home for dinner. At ten-thirty I am in bed."

In the world of the press where habits were so irregular as to be no habits at all, Merrill stuck out as a peculiarity.

He outlived many other editors, nevertheless. By 1904 he was getting ready to retire and Pulitzer was looking for his successor. He talked it over with Samuel M. Williams, one of his secretaries, and complained that good editors were hard to find. Williams objected. There were plenty of good men in the country. Fine! Pulitzer promptly gave him the job of finding one.

For weeks Williams studied every newspaper. He traveled from city to city, reading and studying editorials and news stories, looking for the men who had written them. Finally he found *the* man. It seemed that the writings of one Frank I. Cobb in the Detroit *Free Press* answered every one of Pulitzer's exacting qualifications. He wired his employer about his find.

Pulitzer's prompt wire asked:

WHAT HAS COBB READ IN AMERICAN HISTORY? RHODES, McMASTER, TREVELYAN, PARKMAN? WHAT WORKS ON THE CONSTITUTION AND CONSTITUTIONAL LAW? HAS HE READ BUCKLE'S HISTORY OF CIVILIZATION? WHERE DID HE STAND DURING BRYAN'S FREE SILVER CAMPAIGNS? WHAT ABOUT THE STATE OF HIS HEALTH? HOW TALL IS HE? IS HIS VOICE HARSH OR AGREEABLE? TAKE HIM TO DINNER AND NOTE HIS TABLE MANNERS. IS HIS DISPOSITION CHEERFUL? SOUND OUT HIS AMBITIONS: WHETHER SATISFIED OR LOOKING FOR A LARGER FIELD. BE VERY CAREFUL TO GIVE NO INTIMATION I AM INTERESTED. DESCRIBE MINUTELY HIS APPEARANCE, COLOR OF EYES, SHAPE OF FOREHEAD, MANNERISMS, HOW HE DRESSES. SEARCH HIS BRAIN FOR EVERYTHING THERE IS IN IT.

This was a large order. Williams took Cobb to dinner and sounded him out. The young man, twenty-four years old, tall and muscular and pleasant looking, answered every question with an amazing fund of knowledge. He passed every test—even one which he could have had no idea *was* a test. At the end of the first course Williams leaned back with a sigh of relief. He could write jubilantly to Pulitzer: "He ate soup without a gurgle!"

Cobb took over the main editorial desk at the *World*. Time and again his ideas clashed with those of his employer's; time after time he quit or was fired, repented or was hired back at a bigger salary. For all their battles, the relationship between the two men became almost that of father and son.

The early, startling growth of the *Sunday World* was largely due to the work of Morrill Goddard and still later of Arthur Brisbane. But not only great *men* were on the *World* staff.

One day, in 1878, a tiny girl battled her way for three hours to get past guard and staff to see John Cockerill. Pulitzer happened to be in his own office with the door slightly ajar between his room and Cockerill's. He heard her impassioned plea to become a reporter for the *World*. It was unheard of. Women just did not work for newspapers.

But Joseph Pulitzer was impressed with Nellie Bly's ideas. She wanted to get stories from the inside; to work as a shopgirl, a factory girl, a servant, and then to write these stories for the *World*. He heard in her voice an echo of his own driving enthusiasm as a young reporter in St. Louis. She had the same itch to get the facts no one else had and the same interest in people. She wanted so *badly* to be a reporter! He hired her—on condition she get herself committed to Blackwell's Island, the notorious asylum for the mentally deranged of New York, in order to report honestly on conditions there.

She succeeded in fooling doctors and even the judges who committed her. When she came out ten days later she wrote a story that was a bombshell, exposing the harsh treatment and the horrible conditions on the island.

After that fabulous start, Nellie Bly was given a free hand by Cockerill to write as she pleased. Her exposés were weekly features of the *Sunday World*. She became America's first accredited newspaperwoman, with her own desk in the city room of the nation's biggest newspaper. Pulitzer raised her to international fame when he arranged for her to make a trip around the world to beat the record of Jules Verne's fictional hero of *Around the World in Eighty Days*. Nellie made it in seventy-two days, six hours and ten minutes and set a new world record!

The reasons for the success of the *World* could be seen by a quick glance at the front pages of the New York newspapers for February 8, 1887.

The *Tribune* had no pictures. The type used by the *Times* was uniform; story and heads were crowded together. The *World* used bold headlines, half a dozen drawings, wide white spaces to set off its stories. The *World* had ten pages while the others had four and six.

The big news in that issue of February 8th was a railroad wreck at the town of White River Junction in Vermont. The *World* had four columns on it with eyewitness accounts by a fireman hero who saved half dozen people from death, the words and stories of dozens of the victims, the nurses and the doctors. Drawings showed the scene, the people and the wreck itself.

The *Tribune* had two columns. No eyewitness accounts, no pictures. The *Sun* headlined its account "The Railroad Slaughter" and wrote it vividly, but in only one short column. The *Times* ignored the story completely!

But in 1896 all this was to change. No longer would the *World* be supremely confident of its top circulation. A rival appeared on the scene. From then on Pulitzer's staff must fight to keep their readers.

William Randolph Hearst had once worked for the *World*. When he took over the tiny San Francisco *Examiner* he had written to his father: ". . . it would be well to make the paper as far as possible original, to clip only when absolutely necessary and to imitate only such leading journals as the New York *World*. ..."

Now, with the *Examiner* a booming success, Hearst was ready to invade New York and challenge the paper he considered the best in the country.

Albert Pulitzer had sold his *Morning Journal* to a man named McLean; McLean sold to Hearst. The *Journal* was only a small newspaper with a small plant. Office space had been rented in the Pulitzer Building and it was here, on the eleventh floor, right in the heart of the *World* empire, that Hearst came to lay his plans.

No one saw any danger in his presence there. The *Morning Journal* was too insignificant a sheet to cause any worry. The first indication of trouble exploded like a bomb. Editor Goddard and the entire staff of the *Sunday World* had been hired by Hearst and had already left the Pulitzer Building and set up shop at the plant of the *Journal*.

Cables flew to the publisher's yacht. Pulitzer, furious but desperate, replied: "Hire them back!" An offer was made at higher salaries: back to the *World* trooped Goddard and the rest.

But the game of musical chairs was not finished. Two hours later Hearst had upped the ante once more, and once more the whole crew deserted to the *Journal* building. This time Pulitzer refused to play the game. They could stay with Hearst.

But by now Pulitzer knew that he had a dangerous adversary to cope with. Arthur Brisbane was given Goddard's job as Sunday editor and instructed to go into the fight with everything he had in his power, in order to smash this upstart. It was obvious that Hearst was relying on the Sunday edition to establish himself.

There began a battle of sensationalism such as had never been seen in the press before—or since. Readers ate their Sunday morning breakfasts to such an accompaniment of murder, crime and sex splashed across the pages of both the *World* and the *Journal* that this era gave to dictionaries the phrase "yellow journalism." The term came from one particular battle of the two papers. For a long time the *World* had been famous for introducing the first comic strips. Especially was it noted for the strip called "Hogan's Alley," but which all the readers called by its more familiar name of the "Yellow Kid." Hearst lured the cartoonist to his staff, but the *World* owned the rights to the title, so for a while both newspapers were running the comic strips which featured life in Hogan's Alley.

Finally Pulitzer decided the *World* was going too far. He ordered Brisbane to cut down on the too-sensational stories. It was hopeless to try to smash Hearst and the *World* was losing every shred of dignity in the battle.

A few months later Brisbane, too, deserted to the *Morning Journal*.

Pulitzer held no grudge against Hearst for stealing his editors. It was entirely in keeping with his own practice of constantly searching for the best journalists for his own papers, and he was even guilty of taking away a man from his own St. Louis *Post-Dispatch* if it would benefit his beloved *World*. Such a bit of piracy resulted in the appearance of Charles E. Chapin in the New York office. Chapin was a great editor, a colorful figure. He became the model for the hard-boiled type of editor that was soon to become popular in books and on the stage.

He expected his reporters to get the news even if they had to steal, lie or break their necks to do so. The story is told of him—though it is also credited to other editors—that a reporter once phoned him to say that he was trying to interview a man but the man not only refused, he threatened to beat him up. Chapin told him: "You go back and tell him he can't scare *me!*"

Another time a reporter was late to work. He had used up all his excuses on other occasions. If Chapin wasn't to fire him, this excuse had to be a good one.

"You won't believe this," he told the editor, "but just as I was leaving the apartment house, a fellow came out and said a man had died next door and asked me to please help carry out the corpse."

"Good," Chapin said, "write a story about it. We'll put it on page one."

He knew the story was a lie, but he let the reporter suffer for hours, thinking he was expected to write that story, so that the lesson would sink in.

The New York *Times* and the *Tribune* began to change with the demands of the age. Slowly but solidly they built up their reputation and their circulation. But since the reading public had also grown, the *World* could still hold its own, and when Pulitzer and his editorial staff set out to right a wrong, to expose a scandal— whether it was a local streetcar franchise or a national fraud—then there was no other publication to equal them.

Late in the fall of 1908 the *World* took on its biggest exposé and made its biggest enemy.

Theodore Roosevelt, then President of the United States, had just bought rights to dig the Panama Canal from a French syndicate for forty million dollars. The nation was jubilant. The canal would be a great boon to all civilization. With this point of view the *World* agreed, but there was a mystery surrounding the purchase that bothered Pulitzer and the editors.

Particularly it bothered William Speer, a man on the editorial staff. He began to investigate. Who were the members of this French syndicate? Why was it popularly supposed that the French government had been the ones to negotiate with the American government? Under Speer's probing the story began to unravel.

Years ago France had commissioned a syndicate to explore the possibilities of a canal in Colombia. The syndicate had obtained certain rights and had begun the digging. They abandoned it. The French company had sold out—to whom? A fake revolution had taken place and a strip of land was removed from Colombia and set up as independent Panama.

Who owned the syndicate now? It still had the same French title, but over and over the name of one William Nelson Cromwell began to crop up in Speer's investigations. Then Speer discovered an astounding fact: the French had been paid only twelve million dollars—that was all that had been asked for the rights to the canal—but the syndicate had received forty million dollars from Roosevelt. Where had the rest of the money gone?

Speer wrote an editorial. He put in it all his facts and all his doubts. And he headed it: WHO GOT THE MONEY?

When the story was read to him, Pulitzer ordered Speer to keep asking that question and to ask it until it was answered:

"Who got the money?"

Roosevelt took both editorials and question as a personal libel on his own honesty. Later Pulitzer was to admit that the *World* had gone too far in implicating the President. It was Cromwell and his associates who were suspect—but it was also true that Roosevelt's own brother-in-law was in some way associated with Cromwell's enterprises.

The government drew up a libel suit against Pulitzer and the *World*. Now the question of the Panama Canal was lost in a bigger one: has a president the right to censor a newspaper? What is meant by freedom of the press?

Pulitzer's battle was not just for himself but for all newspapers. He won. The indictments were squashed and Judge Anderson said, as he gave his decision:

It was well stated by a former President of the United States that it is the duty of a newspaper to print the news and tell the truth about it. It is the duty of a public newspaper, such as is owned and conducted by these defendants, to tell the people, its subscribers, its readers, the facts that it may find out about public questions, or matters of public interest; it is its duty and its right to draw inferences from the facts known— draw them for the people....

Neither the people nor the *World* ever did find out the answer to the question of who got the money. A congressional investigation made a halfhearted attempt and came to nothing.

During the long legal fight Frank Cobb was called before a grand jury. The Deputy United States Attorney-General questioned him:

Q. Do you know Mr. Pulitzer?

A. I do.

Q. Did you see him after the President's message of December 15? What did he say about the message?

A. He agreed with me—that it was an attempt to muzzle the paper. . . . Now if the *World* had been intimidated by this libel suit and had shown the white feather, lesser newspapers could hardly be expected to have the courage to criticize the President. . . .

Q. By muzzling you mean—preventing the paper from printing anything it sees fit to print?

A. I mean, preventing the paper from printing that which is its duty as a great newspaper to publish.

The questions of the attorney-general became personal:

Q. When you go to see Mr. Pulitzer, what do you talk about?

A. Mostly about politics, in which he is very deeply interested. But chiefly we discuss the policy of the *World*. Mr. Pulitzer conducts a school of journalism in regard to me. He often says he expects that I shall be able to carry on the principles of the *World* for the next twenty years.

Q. You regard Mr. Pulitzer as the Big Man of the *World*?

A. I regard Mr. Pulitzer as the Big Man of all American newspapers.

ten

Overhead, the clouded sky was steel-gray. In mid-Atlantic the ocean was a smooth and monotonous gray, broken only now and then by the silver plumes of the rising, falling swells. Over this sea the yacht *Liberty* rode, a startling, blinding contrast of gleaming white paint and shining brass.

It was early morning. A steward moved about the library, dusting the bookshelves. His foot caught on a chair leg and made a scraping sound. He looked down, horrified. How could he have forgotten? He was wearing *leather-soled* shoes!—and the library was right over Mr. Pulitzer's bedroom. He had violated one of the strictest rules aboard: to wear nothing but rubber sneakers anywhere on the ship. Quickly he knelt down and slipped the offending shoes off his feet, and tiptoed out to his own cabin.

In the big room below, running the full breadth of the deck space and twenty-five feet long, the man sleeping in the four-poster bed stirred uneasily. He had heard something. A small, scraping sound that had penetrated even through the double thickness of bulkheads and the double doors of his bedroom. He stirred and muttered. One arm stretched out from under the covers. Long, sensitive fingers fumbled for just a fraction of a second with the bedside lamp and then found the electric switch.

Immediately, soft yellow light threw its reflection on his face. The other man in the room, who had been sitting quietly waiting in the shadows, noted the way the light struck the high bones of forehead and cheek and nose, highlighted the strands of silver in the black hair and in the reddish beard. For a second he could even see the blue of one eye—in shocking contrast to the opaque dullness of the other.

Even that blue was an illusion. There was almost no sight behind it.

"Good morning, Mr. Pulitzer."

"Good morning, Dunningham." He was waiting, in tense panic, for a repeating of the scraping sound that had awakened him. When seconds passed and it did not come, he relaxed and smiled. "A *very* good morning. I slept well. And this is an important day, Dunningham."

"I know. A cablegram came late last night from Mrs. Pulitzer. She is in complete agreement with all your plans."

"Dear Kate. Of course she is. We talked it over when I was at Bar Harbor last."

He rose. The two men worked together like an efficient team co-ordinated by long practice. Joseph Pulitzer had learned how to do many things by his sense of touch and hearing. He was now sixty-three years old; it was 1910; he had adjusted his physical world to his needs and knew how to make his way within those limits.

Without stumbling he walked to the washstand. This was built high enough so he did not have to stoop. Dunningham had noticed one day, at the old washstand, that lowering his head brought a painful rush of blood into Pulitzer's eyes.

Jabez E. Dunningham stood in a peculiar relationship to his employer: part nurse, part steward, part diplomat, confidential agent, personal manager and friend. The greatest proof of trust in him was that Pulitzer, pathologically shy of exposing any part of his body, would allow this man to help him dress.

When the famous sculptor Rodin had begun the bust of

169

Pulitzer's head and shoulders there had been a violent, stormy quarrel. Not even for Rodin would he open his collar or loosen his tie.

While the two men worked they talked.

"Did you answer Kate that we would be coming to Chatwold this month?" They had purchased the big estate of Chatwold at Bar Harbor and had built a special "Tower of Silence," a complete wing soundproofed for him there. "I'm hoping Joseph can come on from St. Louis. The *Post-Dispatch* can do without him for a week. It's good to know that he is there and Ralph at the *World*. Even with me at sea, they are still Pulitzer papers. When Herbert grows old enough he'll be a newspaperman, too, I hope."

"It will be pleasant for you to see the grandchildren, too."

Pulitzer chuckled. "The rascals. They think a grandfather who can mount and ride a horse—and teach *them* to ride, too—is an absolute magician."

Dunningham went on to make reports. The ninety-seven-page memorandum had been sent before they left Cap Martin and cables were here from the *World* in answer. It seemed there was a little trouble again.

"Can't they save their 'little troubles'? Can't they spare me those? They know the kind of newspaper we are running! As long as it is honest and fearless and stays independent—" his voice was rising in an angry pitch.

Dunningham saw his mistake and quickly changed the subject.

"The new secretary Mr. Ireland—I think he worries that he hasn't been able to please you. Don't you think I should reassure him?"

Pulitzer's face always registered every emotion he felt. Now he turned toward the other in astonishment, his anger forgotten.

"Why should he think that? I've been no harder on him than on the others. Though, as a matter of fact, I wasn't sure of him until recently. He was too meek. But he gave me a good argument the other day; he will do. I like that. Yes, tell him, by all means. I wouldn't want him to think I don't appreciate the efforts he makes, though he has a lot to learn. If he's going to stay with me he must learn I cannot tolerate sloppy thinking or poor memory or half-digested facts." From his quick sensitivity to his secretary's worries he plunged into an unhappy, moody distress of his own. "I wish they could understand, all of them, what it is like to have to get everything from them secondhand. If they are wrong, then I am wrong—and I *cannot* be wrong! Too much depends on it. They have to be my eyes; I must go through their brains to my own. They are like an extension of myself."

He was angry again—not at the men but at the prison he was in. Every time Dunningham saw him like this, and it was often, he was reminded of a wild eagle struggling against the bars of a cage, wings clipped, the instinct to soar as fierce as ever.

"I know I make them slave, poring over books and newspapers day and night. Don't they realize—"

"They do, Mr. Pulitzer. They realize that you have to work ten times as hard as they. You have to take not one secretary's work, but five—and sort it out, think about it, remember it all, make judgments from it. You can't jot down what you want to know or remember. It all has to be in your head.'

Pulitzer clapped his friend's arm. "Did I sound as if I pitied myself? Well, sometimes I do. But this isn't the day for pity or gloom. Come on, let's breakfast."

Abovedeck, next to the spacious library was the bridge (this odd construction was to keep the men on watch from walking to and fro over Pulitzer's head) and on the other side of the library was the dining room.

This morning there were four men in it. All of them were secretaries: Alleyne Ireland, Norman Graham Thwaites, Friederich Mann, George Craven. Another, William Romaine Paterson, called the "walking encyclopedia" by the others, for his fine memory, was

171

busy going over the cabled news stories that had come that morning and was still in his own cabin.

"Another day. Same routine," Mann sighed. He helped himself to bacon and eggs from the sideboard. "I'll be glad when we arrive at Chatwold; there's more variety and we have more leisure to ourselves."

"And," Craven put in slyly, "how do you spend it? You go to Boston and New York hunting for German novels to amuse J.P. and for new recordings to play for him. This time I am determined I am going to see one theater play just for myself—no trying to remember each scene for him, no analyzing it, no critical attitude— just see a play for my own amusement."

"Don't kid yourself. You'll be repeating it line for line all the way back from the theater. This becomes a habit with us."

"Doesn't the pressure ever relax?" Alleyne was new. He was curious over the intense devotion of these men to their work for Pulitzer. He felt it himself and he was not sure just why: he was paid well but money alone could not have made him stay through the slavery of the work and the passionate tempers he had to face from his employer. Why did he stay? He wasn't sure.

Thwaites answered him. "The only times we can take it easy is when Mrs. Pulitzer and the family come aboard for trips. Herbert was with us for a while last year; J.P. spent a lot of time with him."

Paterson came in, rubbing bleary eyes. "I stayed up until three o'clock this morning," he explained, "reading Rousseau's *Confessions*. I made the mistake yesterday of saying Rousseau left the Hermitage because of a quarrel with Diderot. J.P. challenged me. He was right. Now he's caught me in one mistake he'll go after me hammer and tongs on the rest of it."

"You're lucky this morning. You get the first reading." At breakfast time one of the secretaries just skimmed over the lighter news items in the cabled news dispatches. Later Pulitzer would demand a more intense reading, and the secretary who had that job for the day came in for a real workout, making detailed notes as he went along of the publisher's comments so that an analysis might be prepared for the *World* staff in New York.

Pulitzer walked into the dining room, his arm through Dunningham's. His face was genial. The secretaries relaxed. This was not, then, to be one of those days when his racked nerves made him outrageously demanding, exacting, sarcastic—even cruel. Those days came seldom. Even in the midst of them he could sometimes force himself by sheer iron will to become good tempered. When that happened the men around him were moved to such love and pity they could forgive him anything.

Alleyne Ireland had wondered if that was the reason? Did they stay with J.P. out of pity because he was a tragic figure? It didn't seem the right answer, somehow. . . . It lacked something.

This morning Pulitzer surprised them all. "Ireland, we will let the Macaulay readings go this afternoon. You can read me the essays tomorrow instead."

Instantly they all came alert. Why the change? But Pulitzer said no more. The morning went on as usual.

All of the cabled news had to be read, examined; the answer prepared to send back to the *World*. By eleven-thirty that morning Thwaites was reading back to J.P. the notes they had made:

Good lead on the Kaiser Wilhelm story—tell Cobb not to indulge in fancy guesswork—does he know situation between France and Germany getting worse? Get the facts. Rest of page weak—bank robber described as short—what is short? Four feet? Five feet? Be exact. Electric power utility scandal written too vague—I know the name of every man involved and so do you. Put them in. The *World* protects no one. Editorial on Philippines good—keep it up—the *World* favored war with Spain but should have given them independence immediately afterward—call it by right name—Teddy Roosevelt im-

173

perialism—women suffrage article very poor—ridicule not
effective—

And on and on it went. Then Craven had his turn. It was his
job to read to his employer the backlog of newspapers of all
countries and states that they had picked up in a tremendous
bundle at Cap Martin. Day by day these were sifted.

At luncheon, again, there was a change in the day's schedule.
Pulitzer did not join them for his usual discussion of books and
plays and music. Instead he ate from a tray in the library, behind
closed doors, and they could hear his voice rising and falling as he
talked to Dunningham.

Alleyne Ireland asked the others: "Why does he demand so
much study from us? I can understand that he would work us
hard over newspaper reports; that's his job. But I sometimes feel
he doesn't have us read books or discuss plays with him for his
entertainment; he puts us through the hoops."

"Sometime," Paterson explained, "he will tell you the story of
a boy in St. Louis and a teacher by the name of Thomas Davidson.
You are right. He wants to make us learn and think. It's diversion
for him, too. He flogs his mind, drives it to the point of exhaustion.
If he isn't thinking, then he has too much time to feel and then
he falls into those moods of gloom and despair and self-pity—he
keeps his mind going to avoid them."

After lunch Friederich Mann slipped away to the library. Soon
through the closed door came the soft strains of the Brahms "Lul-
laby." Dunningham came out. As he opened the door Ireland
caught a glimpse of Pulitzer on the couch, an afghan pulled over
him. Mann sat slightly behind his head and read, softly, a German
novel. His voice was gradually dropping lower and softer. From the
couch came the whisper:

"*Leise, ganz leise—ganz leise* (softly, quite softly). . . ." Pulitzer
murmured as he drifted into sleep.

174

Dunningham joined Ireland on the deck and the two men walked while Dunningham told the other of J.P.'s good opinion of him. The new secretary found himself pleased out of all proportion to the compliment. Why? he wondered again. Is it because he is older and because we on board live a sort of family life, with him playing the role of father?

"I hope he sleeps today. He has an important announcement to make later this afternoon and he wants all of us to gather in the library. If he sleeps now, the excitement may not be too much for him; I hope so. Strange that music can soothe him while other sounds are torture. It is the unexpected noise, the sharp, crackling, scraping, shrill noise that bothers him so much. That reminds me, Ireland. I don't like to mention it but you may have noticed we no longer serve almonds after dinner?"

"Yes. I was going to speak to you about it. I am very fond of almonds."

"We discontinued serving them until I had an opportunity to speak to you. You have a habit of breaking them in two before eating them. The snap of breaking them affects Mr. Pulitzer as disastrously as if you fired a pistol right in his ear."

"Oh, I'm terribly sorry!"

"No need to be. It embarrasses him that he is so sensitive to these things and he can't bring himself to speak to you himself. That's my job. All of us have had to adjust simple, ordinary things we do to make life a little more bearable for him."

Could it be, Ireland pondered, precisely the strangeness, the weirdness, of this life that attracted him and held him to a most difficult job?

At three o'clock the summons came for the staff to be in the library. One by one they filed in and saw that chairs had been arranged in a semicircle around J.P.'s desk. They took their places. A moment later he walked in and seated himself, facing them. He took a sheaf of papers from Dunningham and arranged them by a

175

sense of touch so that they spread fanwise on the desk. A slight tension gripped the spectators as he fumbled for a moment among the papers, selected one particular bound document by the weight and feel of it and handed it to Dunningham.

Pulitzer cleared his throat. "Gentlemen," he said, "I have asked you to come in here for a special reason. I am going to read you my will." There was a low murmur of surprise through the room but he checked it by raising his hand slightly. "I mean, of course, that Mr. Dunningham will read it to you."

Dunningham began reading:

I, Joseph Pulitzer, of the City of New York, being of sound mind, do make, publish and declare—

Pulitzer interrupted him. "The legal language, I am afraid, is tiring to me and boring to others. Perhaps it would be better, gentlemen, if I simply told you the important bequests in it. I should like to explain them, too, since some are of a rather startling nature. I will start with the minor ones first: there will be one, not quite a million dollars, to the Philharmonic Society of New York—you see, Friederich, my interest in music is not just an old man's self-indulgence. There will be another legacy of the same amount to the Metropolitan Museum of Art. Twenty-five thousand dollars for a statue of Thomas Jefferson—the city can put it anywhere they please, for all I care."

He smiled to himself. "I have had some arguments over this statue. My friends feel it is a waste of money. A statue! Why not give the money to a hospital, perhaps? But I feel that not enough honor is paid to the man who is most responsible for our concept of American democracy. If it had not been for Jefferson, the Constitution and the Bill of Rights might well have been scraps of paper. He headed the revolt of the American people against the Alien and Sedition Acts; it is his concept of democracy that I believe in, that

176

no man should be prosecuted for what he thinks or believes. Thomas Jefferson has always been a guide to me."

From his pocket he took a cigar and rolled it, lovingly, between his fingers. His doctor forbade him to smoke except after dinner, but just for today he was going to disobey orders. As he lit it, Ireland felt that discipline had relaxed enough so that he, too, could light his pipe.

When Pulitzer spoke again his voice was no longer genial. It had become intense. His face lifted. His sightless eyes seemed to be seeing visions beyond the limits of the room. "I have left for the *World* a trust fund so it may live on forever. The *World* was never just a financial enterprise. It must continue forever to be the champion of the people, for good against evil, for honesty against corruption. The money I have put in trust for it will not be enough to insure its life, but we have proved that a newspaper founded on real democratic ideals and the good of the nation can also prosper on its own. My own life is mortal; the *World* must be immortal."

Never before had the men facing him been so struck with the majesty and the sublime dignity of his face.

He went on: "There is another bequest even dearer to my heart. I would like to help train newspapermen to become real journalists, to realize their duty and obligation and responsibility to the readers for whom they publish. For this they must be educated men. I have long had an idea. It has been called impossible, ridiculous, fantastic. But I have finally persuaded the trustees of Columbia University that it is not so farfetched as it sounds and they are ready to accept it. I am giving now, before my death, two million dollars to the Columbia University, in New York, to found a School of Journalism."

There was a ripple of astonished surprise in the room; an involuntary shifting, nervously, in seats. A *school* of journalism?

"The school will also be a memorial to my beloved daughter Lucille Irma, and will carry her name."

Ireland felt a quick rush of tenderness and sympathy. J.P.'s voice had broken, grief stricken, at the mention of this oldest daughter, this daughter who had been so like him, and who had died so suddenly when she was seventeen, a young and lovely and spirited girl.

Then the big head lifted again. The face of Pulitzer changed from sadness to one that showed a slight smile. As if he had read their minds he knew their questions about the school.

"I know. You are thinking: it has never been done before. People will laugh and say that newspapermen are born, not made. They are word-scribblers and the School of Hard Knocks is the only one they need. I agree that the best classroom for a newspaperman is the experience, the learning from life and from the people he is writing for. Perhaps newspapermen are born with certain characteristics of curiosity and inquisitiveness that direct them to their profession; but it is not enough. Observation is not enough. They have to be taught to express themselves clearly, to know the difference between a straight news story and a human-interest story, to learn what makes one page interesting in its make-up and another dull. But the main reason for a School of Journalism is to teach young men and women to *think*. To give them a wide knowledge. How can a man write editorials—the editorials that are the heartbeat of a newspaper—unless he knows something of history and poetry and science and geography and philosophy and the arts? That is what my School of Journalism will give them."

Thwaites had been with his employer long enough to interrupt. "But won't that mean that newspaper editors and reporters will be coming only from the well-to-do families who can afford college educations for them?"

A shadow of pain crossed Pulitzer's face. "I thought of that. I would not want that to happen. The best I can do is also, in my will, to provide for scholarships to the school. And to encourage better standards for newspapermen and for literary men in America

178

I am leaving money for prize awards to be given each year for the outstanding novel of American life, the outstanding newspaper story, the outstanding editorial, the best poem—and so forth—that will advance the cause of democracy."

While the roomful of men was silently thinking over these bequests of the will—and to most of them the idea of a school was truly fantastic!—Pulitzer rose from his chair and walked to the fireplace. One hand groped for the mantelpiece, found it and steadied himself by it. With his back turned he spoke to Ireland:

"Mr. Ireland, you have not been long enough with me to form prejudices. You are not a newspaperman. I would like to have your opinions."

"I think the will is magnificent!" he said enthusiastically. The other men looked at him, surprised. "I think it may do for journalism what Pasteur did for medicine and what Shakespeare did for the stage. It will raise journalism from being a job that men drift into or a vehicle that men can use to promote some selfish interest of their own. Journalism will become a profession, with dignity. And a newspaper will someday be recognized as a weapon as mighty as a sword and as illuminating as a lantern coming into a dark room."

Pulitzer was pleased, but he smiled in an amused way. "You are young, Mr. Ireland, and therefore given to extravagances. I hope you are right. But if you are even partly right, then my life and work is not a failure. . . ." His voice rose suddenly in passion: "Something will go on! The *World* was not perfect. We made mistakes. We backed the wrong candidate sometimes and we failed because we were human and sometimes because we, too, were selfish. There is more good work we have left undone than we have done; more of the rights of the people still needing justice than we have heeded. I have lost faith at times because it seems to me there is no balance: the rich get more and more power, the poor lose more and more rights. Can't we make democracy work for all? We must

179

keep trying!—that is all I know! I will not be here but I want to leave a newspaper that will go on fighting, a school that will teach, and money to help those who need it!"

Dunningham touched him on the arm. Passion and fire were burning up his strength; when he turned away to leave the room on Dunningham's arm his steps faltered and dragged.

And now Ireland knew the answers to his question: Why did men, secretaries or newspapermen, work like slaves for this Joseph Pulitzer? It was not just pity for his blindness. It was not just the response of men to the fatherly interest that Pulitzer took in eager and young minds.

It was because, in spite of tragedy, Pulitzer had risen above it. In spite of his blindness he saw more than most people. In spite of a sick body his mind was powerful. In spite of his wealth he identified himself with those less fortunate. In spite of his handicaps he was still a mighty figure in journalism. In spite of his exile he was one of the foremost men of the country he loved so dearly.

He was a great man.

One year later on October 29, 1911, the *Liberty* lay at anchor off Charleston, South Carolina. Joseph Pulitzer was dying. His last words as he sank gratefully into eternal sleep were the same as those he used to whisper to Mann as the music played after luncheon: *"Leise, ganz leise—ganz leise—"* and *softly, quite softly,* without pain, Death came to him.

Ireland heard the news on deck. He turned away, blindly, from Dunningham's anguished face. He walked to the side of the ship, gripped the railing and bowed his head. He cried, just as every person on board was crying, for the great man who was at last at peace.

In 1931 other men and women wept. It was not an uncommon thing for journalists to see newspapers come and go, to see them flourish and then die away. They weren't by nature immortal. If a newspaper couldn't meet the competition, it either had to be sold, merged with another or fold up entirely. Hard-boiled journalists took this for granted. But not the *World!* This was a paper like no other. J.P.'s will had said it was not to be sold; it was to be considered almost a public trust. His three sons—Ralph, Joseph and Herbert—were to see to it that the *World* lived forever.

Yet all through the summer and fall and winter of 1930 rumors had been flying around the Pulitzer Building that the paper was going to be sold. Although they were denied, they persisted. The staff had become alarmed, first, when Ralph had resigned the presidency of the Pulitzer Press and Herbert had taken his place.

Everyone knew that Ralph was devoted to the *World*, just as Joseph, out in St. Louis, was heart and soul in love with the St. Louis *Post-Dispatch*. But Herbert? The younger son had been only sixteen years old, and still a schoolboy, when his father died. He had never worked on a newspaper under his father's supervision, as the other two had, and he had never absorbed any of his father's passion for journalism. "Young Marster Herbert" the reporters called him, looking upon him as a typical rich man's son who liked to mingle with society and shoot big game in far-off parts of the world—now that he was grown to manhood.

Herbert as president, Ralph ill, and the business of the nation—including the business of running newspapers—in the grip of the worst depression America had ever known—no wonder there were rumors! The staff of the *World* were stunned at first. They couldn't believe it. The paper had been going downhill for the past few years, true; but it had survived other depressions. It wasn't that they were afraid for their jobs. Experienced newspaper people like themselves were in demand anywhere. They could find work. It was more than that: this paper was as dear to them as were their own families, their religion, their very selves. They knew the paper wasn't making as much money as it used to, so they pooled their small savings and borrowed more and offered it all to Herbert.

"Let us buy in!" they begged him. "We'll not only run the *World*; we'll help support it during this emergency. But don't sell the *World*!

He refused. The sale went through. Roy Howard, of the Scripps-Howard chain, bought it. It was merged with another paper to become the *World-Telegram*. (Some years later this combination was to merge again and take over what was left of old Dana's *Sun*, to become the *World-Telegram* and *Sun*.)

That last night of its old life, under its old name, all of the *World* employees—editors, reporters, copyreaders, typesetters, compositors, stereotypers, artists, pressmen, mailing-room workers, deliverymen, office boys—worked with the same shock and anger and hurt in their faces. Tomorrow, March 8th, they would no longer be there. All of them had cried, or come close to it. Now some were tight lipped and angry; some paused in their work to wipe away tears they couldn't keep back; others cursed at the betrayal of old J.P.'s will. For how many years had it been their proudest boast to say: "I am ——— of the *World!*" No matter how any of them now felt, they were all agreed on one thing: this last issue of the *World* was to be their best. Not one inaccurate statement; not one typographical error; no slipshod make-up of the pages—the best they had in them was their last tribute to Joseph Pulitzer.

One by one, as the work was finished, lights were switched off in room after room. A man walked slowly out of the big front doors. He passed a group of reporters lingering on the sidewalks, and he knew they were talking—as they would reminisce for the rest of their lives—of the great stories, the glorious past, of the *World*. His own footsteps sounded hollow and ghostly where so many feet had rushed back and forth for so many years. Tomorrow the lights would go on again; the Pulitzer Building would not go unused. But never again would he walk in and out of there; never again would he say: "I am Barrett of the *World!*"

It was easy to understand these emotions of bitterness from the staff. They loved this paper.

What they did not see was that the Pulitzer family had taken the only way they thought possible to keep the *World* from going under entirely. Huge newspaper chains were gobbling up almost all family-owned papers; only a bold publisher could hope to guide an independent newspaper through these stormy financial days. Joseph, Jr. was such a man but his heart was with the *Post-Dispatch* —and he was wise enough to know he could not maintain both papers. Only his father could have done that.

Ralph was unquestionably a fine writer and reporter, but he was not an administrator. Herbert was shrewd in financial matters, but he had none of the bold vision, none of the newspaper experience, of his pioneer father. Without the guiding spirit of its founder, the *World* was doomed. The brothers decided to hold onto the *Post-Dispatch* and let the New York *World* go.

It was irony that the St. Louis paper, the first Pulitzer paper— but the one the father had come to ignore and slight—should be the one to carry on the Pulitzer tradition. Joseph, Jr. had inherited much of his father's special temperament. He had quit school in his sophomore year; J.P. had banished him to St. Louis to "teach him a lesson." To everyone's surprise, the young man had been captured by both the city and the paper. He never wanted to leave it.

And today, his sons, Joseph Pulitzer's grandsons, carry on one of the finest newspapers in the United States. Still in the family, the St. Louis *Post-Dispatch* is edited and managed in the tradition of fearless and liberal journalism.

And because it is still so today, we have the right to imagine that on some still, quiet night the tall ghost of Joseph Pulitzer comes back to visit his first newspaper. Heaven would not be good and just if the founder of the *Post-Dispatch* could not sometimes look in and see that all was well.

A modern building, a well-run building—the red beard nods approvingly. This was where Briggs once bumped the forms down the shaky stairs because the elevator wasn't working! The ghost would be sure to smile with astonishment at the new, huge presses. Even better than those that were once the pride of the *World*! And in the lobby, on the counter, he might stand to pore over the week's copies of the *Post-Dispatch,* bound so that visitors like himself could read them easily.

A practiced eye might glance over the front page. Good! The paper boasted of sixty-four pages; that was a lot more than he himself had been able to achieve for this St. Louis paper. Price five cents— a lot of money—the *World* had always sold for two cents. But, then, everything was more expensive than in his day. The front page was nicely balanced between international stories, national stories and local news. Plenty of good pictures. The ghost might fret a little, turning page after page. Were the facts straight? Was the news fresh? He needn't worry—he knows that—young Joseph is a good newspaperman—but he cannot help himself. The pages turn on and in those pages the ghost of Joseph Pulitzer might read a news story with his name in it. It might be the announcement of the year's Pulitzer Prize awards, those awards so eagerly sought after by novelists and poets and dramatists, journalists, historians and philosophers, those awards which have done so much to raise the standards of creative writing and profound thought in America.

Or again, a page would turn and it might be the story of college graduations. The tall ghost straightens proudly. Schools of Journalism everywhere! How everyone had laughed and scorned his idea of a School of Journalism! Even Columbia University had hesitated to accept his gift at first. A crackpot notion, it had been called then. But now the Columbia School of Journalism is an accepted, highly reputed school. It has turned out thousands of trained journalists for the nation's newspapers and has been, in turn, copied by nearly every American college or university. Now all have their journalism departments.

The pages turn on. J.P. is looking, anxiously, for the editorial page. Next he looks for the special writers, and finds them: three full pages! The names of the columnists are strange to him: Drew Pearson, Thomas L. Stokes, William J. Humphreys, Anthony Leviero, Doris Fleeson, Marguerite Higgins. Two women! And the lips above the red beard smile fondly, remembering the lone girl who first battled her way into his office and who pioneered for women reporters—his Nellie Bly. His eye moves on to scan the editorials: social security, civil rights, mediation between steel strikers and employers, better schools—the ghost of Joseph Pulitzer is satisfied. The *Post-Dispatch* is still fighting on the side of the people.

Then he sees it: the tiny box up in the left-hand corner on the editorial page. It reads:

ST. LOUIS POST-DISPATCH

Founded by Joseph Pulitzer
December 12, 1878
Published by
The Pulitzer Publishing Company

Under it is the statement he himself had written when his blindness had taken him away from actual, physical management of the paper. Forty-five years after his death—and still printed:

THE POST-DISPATCH PLATFORM

I know that my retirement will make no difference in its cardinal principles; that it will always fight for progress and reform, never tolerate injustice or corruption, always fight demagogues of all parties, never belong to any party, always oppose privileged classes and public plunderers, never lack sympathy with the poor, always remain devoted to the public welfare; never be satisfied with merely printing news; always be drastically independent; never be afraid to attack wrong, whether by predatory plutocracy or predatory poverty.

JOSEPH PULITZER

April 10, 1907

And as it was true then, so it is true today of the St. Louis *Post-Dispatch*. The pages close; the ghost is happy.

bibliography

BARRETT, JAMES WYMAN. The End of the World. New York and London: Harper and Bros., 1931

BARRETT, JAMES WYMAN. The World, the Flesh, and Messrs. Pulitzer. New York: Vanguard Press, 1941

BARRETT, JAMES WYMAN. Joseph Pulitzer and His World. New York: Vanguard Press, 1941

BEARD, CHARLES A. American Government and Politics. New York: The MacMillan Company, 1928

BENT, SILAS. Newspaper Crusaders. New York and London: Whittlesey House, McGraw Hill, 1939

BIRD, GEORGE LLOYD AND MERWIN, FREDERIC E. The Newspapers and Society. New York: Prentice-Hall, 1942

BLEYER, WILLARD GROSVENOR. Main Currents in the History of American Journalism. Boston: Houghton, Mifflin Co., 1927

BROWN, HENRY COLLINS. Brownstone Fronts and Saratoga Trunks. New York: E. P. Dutton and Co., 1935

CARLSON, OLIVER. Brisbane, a Candid Biography. New York: Stackpole Sons, 1937

IRELAND, ALLEYNE. An Adventure with a Genius. New York: E. P. Dutton and Co., 1938

JOSEPHSON, MATTHEW. The Politicos. New York: Harcourt Brace and Co., 1938

NOBLE, IRIS. Nellie Bly, First Woman Reporter. New York: Julian Messner, Inc., 1956

SALMON, LUCY MAYNARD. The Newspaper and the Historian. New York: Oxford University Press, 1923

SEITZ, DON CARLOS. Joseph Pulitzer, His Life and Letters. New York, Simon and Schuster, 1924

187

index

Adams, Franklin P., 159
Anderson, Maxwell, 159
Arsenal Island, 49
Augustine, Captain Edward, 78-80

Bartholdi, Auguste, 141
Bennett, Mr., 124, 126, 138
Blau, Max (stepfather), 14, 18, 20, 85
Bly, Nellie, 161-162, 185
Boston, 7-10, 11
Brachvogel, Udo, 44-45
Briggs, Mr., 96, 100, 103-104, 110
Brisbane, Arthur, 161, 163-164
Broun, Heywood, 159
Budapest, Hungary, 11, 14, 19, 35, 46, 85, 86

Carvalho, Mr., 150, 151
Chapin, Charles E., 164-165
City Hall Park, 17
Cleveland, Grover, 137-138, 140
Clopton, William H., 113-114
Cobb, Frank I., 160-161, 167, 173
Cobb, Irvin S., 159
Cockerill, John A., 111-112, 113-114, 116, 132, 133-136, 139-140, 145, 147, 149-150, 151, 157, 161
Columbia University, School of Journalism, 177-179, 184-185
Conestoga wagon, 39
Craven, George, 171-172, 174

Dana, Charles, 91, 125-126, 138, 146-149
Danube River, 19
Davidson, Thomas, 45-49, 50-52, 61-62, 71, 76, 81, 87-88, 91, 104, 112, 125, 149-150, 174
Davis, Colonel William, 152, 157

Davis, William Worthington, 92
Democratic party, 64-65, 70, 74, 84, 120, 123, 133, 137-138, 140, 146, 147
Dillon, John, 97-101, 107-108, 111, 116, 157
Dispatch, St. Louis, 58, 80, 94-97, 99
Dunningham, Jabez E., 169-170, 174-176, 180

Engelman, Dr. George, 51
Examiner, San Francisco, 162

Fleeson, Doris, 185
freedom of the press, 166

German, 10, 12, 13, 17-19, 28, 32, 34, 36, 42, 44, 49, 53, 76, 84
Goddard, Morrill, 161, 163
Gould, Jay, 123
Grant, President, 65, 81, 120
Greeley, Horace, 81, 125
Gruelle, Walter, 80

Hamburg, Germany, 10-11, 20
Hearst, William Randolph, 162-164
Herald, New York, 118, 123, 126-127, 128, 129, 133, 138, 145
Higgins, Marguerite, 185
Howard, Roy, 182
Humphreys, William J., 185
Hurlbert, William Henry, 124, 126-130, 132, 133
Hyde, Colonel W. B., 109

immigrants, 10-11, 34, 44, 49, 54
Ireland, Alleyne, 170-173, 174-175, 177, 178, 179, 180

Jefferson, Thomas, 176-177
Jefferson City, Missouri, 69-71, 74, 77-80

Koeppler, Arthur, 51, 72-73, 88-89, 102, 106
Ku Klux Klan, 143

Lazarus, Emma, 143
Leviero, Anthony, 185
Lincoln, Abraham, 17, 27, 31, 54
Lincoln Cavalry, 17-18, 20-22, 23-31, 54
Lippmann, Walter, 159

McGuffin, Mr., 112, 133-136
McLane, Doctor, 153
Mackay, Sergeant, 10-11
Makó, Hungary, 13, 19
Mann, Friederich, 171-172, 174, 176
Mercantile Library, 42, 44-45, 49, 52
Merrill, William H., 159-160
Metropolitan Museum of Art, 176
Mitchell, Dr. S. Weir, 153, 154
Morning Journal, 118-119, 127, 163-164

New York City, 11-12, 15, 16-17, 31-35, 86, 117-127, 128-132, 133, 136, 138, 140-143, 145, 146, 151, 154, 176
Nicoll, De Lancy, 146-147

Panama Canal, 165-166
Patterson, William Romaine, 171, 174
Pearson, Drew, 185
Philharmonic Society of New York, 176
Piel, Colonel, 23-24, 30
Politzer, Albert (brother), 18-20, 34, 85-86, 118, 123, 163
Politzer, Irma (sister), 18
Politzer, Mrs. Louise (mother), 11, 14, 18-20, 29, 31, 34, 85
Politzer, Philip (father), 14, 18-20
Ponsonby, Claude, 151-154
Post, St. Louis, 95, 97, 98
Post-Dispatch, St. Louis, 98-116, 122, 125, 127, 144, 150, 164, 181, 183-186
Pouletzes, Joseph. *See* Pulitzer, Joseph

Preetorius, Dr. Emil, 49, 52-56, 63-64, 66, 69, 71-72, 81-83, 84
Pulitzer, Constance (daughter), 154
Pulitzer, Edith (daughter), 154
Pulitzer, Herbert (son), 170, 172, 181-182, 183
Pulitzer, Joseph
  his arrival in Boston, 7-11; birthplace, 13; family, 14, 18-20; description of, at 17, 15-16; at 19, 48; at 21, 67; at 22, 76; at 31, 89; at 43, 155; at 63, 169-171; arrives in New York, 16; enlists in Union Army, 17, 20; childhood and youth, 18-20; his life as a soldier, 23-31; looks for work, 32-34; goes to St. Louis, 35; works at various jobs, 40-41, 48-51; studies law, 45; makes lifelong friend, 45-48; passes law examinations, 51; meets Carl Schurz, 53; is hired as reporter, 57; is disliked by editor, 62, 66, 68-69; his story catches criminal, 63; looks for stories, 66-67; is considered outstanding, 67-69, 72; covers state legislature, 70-71; makes suggestions for changes, 72; earns reputation, 73-74; grows beard, 76; is elected to state legislature, 74-77; exposes graft and corruption, 77-80; is involved in shooting, 79-80; is appointed a police commissioner, 81; campaigns for Horace Greeley, 81; is part owner of *Westliche Post,* 82-83; makes changes, 84; sells his interest because of poor health, 84-85; visits family, 85-86; moves to hotel, 87; is considered eligible young man, 89-91; is delegate to Constitutional Convention, 90-91; his formula, 90-91; is special correspondent for *Sun,* 91; falls in love, 91; looks for opening in journalism, 93; marries, 94; buys the *Dispatch,* 95; merges with *Post,* 98; his statement of principle, 99-100; introduces new kind of journalism, 101-105; continues as reformer, 107; is bodily attacked, 108-109; sets killing pace, 110; is now sole owner, 111; his children, 112-113, 154; moves to larger building, 113;

Pulitzer, Joseph (continued)
misses children by being busy, 113;
paper is attacked, 115; takes vacation, 117; doctors advise complete
rest, 119; buys New York *World*,
126; is its editor, 127-132; approves
new make-up, 134-136; his platform, 136-137; launches presidential
campaign, 137-138; passes circulation of all papers, 139; is elected to
Congress, 140; his younger daughter
dies, 140; starts Statue of Liberty
fund, 141-143; crusades against discrimination, 143; expands paper,
145; is maliciously attacked, 146-
148; is losing eyesight, 149-151;
purchases new building site, 151;
takes boat trip to rest nerves, 151;
is blind in one eye, 153; must separate himself from family and active
life, 153-156, 158; begins life on
yacht, 156; remains active, 158-161;
173; battles with Hearst, 163-164;
is sensitive to slightest noise, 168,
175; his life on yacht, 169-175; his
will, 176-180; dies, 180; his *World*
sold, 180-183; his tradition carried
on in *Post-Dispatch*, 183-186
Pulitzer, Jr., Joseph (son), 154, 157,
170, 181, 183
Pulitzer, Kate Davis (wife), 91-94, 97,
98-99, 103, 106, 108-109, 110-113,
115-116, 117-126, 139-141, 147,
149-151, 153-155, 169
Pulitzer, Katherine Ethel (daughter),
113, 118, 140
Pulitzer, Lucille Irma (daughter), 113,
118, 154, 177-178
Pulitzer Prize awards, 179, 184
Pulitzer, Ralph (son), 112-113, 118,
140, 154, 170, 181, 183

Ramsay, Captain, 23-27, 29-30
Raymond, Mr., 125
Republican party, 53, 64, 70, 74-77,
81, 84, 120
Rodin, 169-170
Roosevelt, Theodore, 143, 165-167
Roslein's Bookstore, 51, 57-61, 62-63,
65

St. Louis, Missouri, 34-37, 38-40, 42-
44, 49, 51, 54, 55, 57, 60, 62, 65,
66, 67, 70-71, 74-78, 81, 84, 85, 87-
88, 90, 94, 95, 99, 101, 104-105,
107, 114-115, 120, 121, 150, 181
Schmidt, Sergeant, 17, 22
Schurz, Carl, 49, 52-56, 62-64, 69, 71-
72, 74, 81-83, 84
Seitz, Don, 159
Sheehan, Winfield R., 159
Slayback, Colonel Alonzo W., 113
Smith, Ballard, 145, 158
Speer, William, 165-166
Stallings, Laurence, 159
Statue of Liberty, 141-143
Stokes, Thomas L., 185
Sun, New York, 91, 120, 123, 124,
126-127, 138, 146-149, 162
Swope, Herbert Bayard, 159

Taylor, Deems, 159
Terhune, Albert Payson, 159
Thwaites, Norman Graham, 171-172,
178
Times, New York, 123-214, 126-127,
129, 133, 138, 162, 165
Tribune, New York, 126-127, 133,
138, 162, 165
Turner, George, 157

Union Army, 10-11, 17-18, 20-31

Vienna, Austria, 11

Walton, Lester A., 159
Washington, Booker T., 143
Washington, D.C., 31, 86, 87, 91, 94,
120, 140
Westliche Post, 49, 54-56, 57-74, 78,
80, 81-83, 84-85, 101, 107
Williams, Samuel M., 160-161
Willich, Louis, 55-58, 59, 61, 62-63,
64, 66-70, 71, 82, 84
Woerner, Judge J. G., 51, 72-73
World, New York, 123, 125, 126-144,
145-149, 151-152, 156, 157-167,
173, 177, 179, 181, 183, 184
World-Telegram and Sun, New York,
182

191

About the Author

IRIS NOBLE grew up on a ranch in the Crow's Nest Pass between Canada's Alberta and British Columbia. Her parents were American and when she was eleven they moved to Oregon. After graduating from the University of Oregon, she moved to Los Angeles and got her first job as a secretary at station KFI-KECA. She left there to work for Fawcett Publications and later was publicity director for a theatre-restaurant. After her marriage she came to New York City where she did freelance writing. In recent years she has made her home in San Francisco and has been devoting herself to writing both in the field of biography and teenage fiction.